570

D1474683

The Heart of the Earth

THE HEART
OF
THE EARTH

O. M. Phillips
Professor of Geophysical Mechanics
at The Johns Hopkins University

 Freeman, Cooper & Company
1736 Stockton Street
San Francisco 94133

Printed in the United States of America

Library of Congress Catalogue Card Number 68-14223

Preface

The interior of the earth is a most tantalizing place to explore. Nothing can be seen directly; to discover its nature we must assemble fragments of evidence of many different kinds and seek their significance using all our resources of imagination and logic. This book is an account of the exploration and of the puzzles that we encounter on the way. It was written for my own pleasure and that of my wife, to whom it is dedicated, but my hope is that it may now give pleasure and stimulus to others.

The writing of any book involves many people, but there are some whom I must acknowledge: Dr. and Mrs. Blair Kinsman for encouraging the conception by persuading me that it was worth doing, Mrs. Marjorie Elder for her untiring work on the manuscript, Mr. James K. Levorsen for his skill in the preparation of the illustrations and finally Mr. John Gallagher and Mrs. Fannia Weingartner for their enthusiasm and assistance in the production of the book. To these and many others, I am most grateful.

O.M.P.

Baltimore
January 1968

Contents

The Heart of the Earth

For Merle

1

The Nature of the Search

The world of our common experience is, in the large, almost two-dimensional. It may encompass the entire surface of the earth, yet it is only a few miles high and perhaps not a mile in depth. This thin shell of space has been our world, where generations have lived and died, species have come and gone. We can look up beyond it to the clouds and the stars; we look *down* to see only the earth at our feet. We can at least see what is above us, but we see nothing at all of what lies beneath us. The deep interior of the earth has been a place of mystery and fascination for time immemorial. In antiquity, Hades was there, the home of dead souls beyond the black river Styx. In the last century, Jules Verne wrote of an imaginary journey from Iceland to Stromboli, through glittering caverns and across dark, malevolent lakes that lie deep inside the earth; although a somewhat implausible tale, it is a gripping one.

What *is* at the heart of the earth? And how do we find out? It is only four thousand miles away but we shall never see it— men may travel to the far planets before they see the center of their own. We cannot explore as Jules Verne imagined since the deepest cavern is a mere pothole on the surface of the earth and the deepest drilling a pinprick. The exploration must be of another kind; a journey of the mind. From our vantage point on the surface of the earth, by measuring and observing we will seek evidences on the nature of the stuff that lies in those 4000 miles beneath us and on the forces that bear upon it. We shall find clues of many kinds; some are obvious and some subtle. Like the pieces of a jig-saw puzzle, they must fit together. Each has a tiny part of the pattern which, if we have the wit to see it and to put it in its place, will add a little to the picture and clarify some part of the design.

The study of the earth is called Geophysics. It is a branch of science that includes many disciplines, many talents, whose interplay provides its characteristic texture. The geologist and the chemist, the physicist, the mathematician and the engineer have all contributed. Yet it is a discipline of its own, and in the shaping of its structure, two attributes in particular have been of enduring importance.

In the first place, its roots are primarily observational, not experimental. In experiment, one essential ingredient is control. The power of experiment lies in the isolation of one phenomenon or effect to the exclusion of others, in the simplification of nature by this control. For example, in a study of the motion of a pendulum, we are at liberty to do the experiment in a quiet room, so that the wind does not disturb it, to choose a firm support which will not wobble, a heavy bob and a long cord so that the friction of the air will retard the motion only slowly. We can vary at will the length of the pendulum and the amplitude of the swing to discover how these separately influence the motion. In geophysics, control is rarely possible. An earthquake may shake a city, or a volcano erupt; we can observe what happens but we cannot control it. We can record as carefully as possible not only the happening but all the information that we believe might be relevant (and possibly some that might not). Then we must wait for the next time and the next, seeking a pattern, or a system, or a relation among all the factors that are involved. Sometimes, some element of control is possible. Explosions can be detonated at a precise time and place, and the reverberations inside the earth can be felt and recorded. But there is neither knowledge nor control of the structure in which the reverberations take place; as with an ailing television set, we bang it to see what happens. Sometimes, what happens is a clue to what is inside, and (in the geophysical context, at least) this is the purpose of experiments of this kind. A seismic prospector might infer in this way that there could be oil below, but his experiment is far from controlled in the way that the pendulum was. Extraneous variables may influence his results in unknown ways; the variability of his results may be much greater than their consistency. Nevertheless, the patient and careful accumulation of observational data, with all its deficiencies and irregularities, is one of the roots of geophysics without which it could not thrive.

Yet this alone is not science. The observations provide only the raw material; the task here is to interpret those that are relevant, to seek in them any clue that may pertain to the nature of the heart of the earth. Often the search begins by asking the right question—"why are things as they are?"—and having no satisfaction until the answer is found. Science is never just an accumulation of facts, or of complicated and tedious theories. Its essence is imagination, the ability to perceive connections between the apparently unrelated, and to see simplicity in apparent confusion. The greatest contributions, like those to literature and art, have required imagination of the highest order, guided always by observation, the rules of logic and the desire for unity and simplicity. This is particularly true in geophysics, where we must often proceed by inference, and not by pure deduction. This second attribute of the subject is, indeed, a consequence of the first. Only the effect is observed; we must *infer* from it the nature of the cause.

It is important to appreciate the distinction between deduction and scientific inference. Deduction is the logical process by which, under a given set of axioms or circumstances, a theorem is proved. Unless there is a mistake, the theorem is true within the axioms and will remain true forever. There is no room for debate; it is a certainty. Different sets of axioms and circumstances will lead to different theorems, and this is the stuff of mathematics. The mathematician is of course concerned with the consistency of his axioms—they must not contradict one another

—but not with the question of their 'correctness' or 'truth.' For him, this is a meaningless notion; the axioms may have been suggested by something in the world around him, but once they are formulated and properly stated, it is they and they alone that form the basis for the subsequent mathematics. Of course, if the axioms correspond closely to the appearances of the world in which we live, then so will the theorems. Elementary Euclidean geometry in 3-dimensions is so useful in practical concerns simply because this is so. However, one can also study Euclidean geometry in 4-dimensions, or 5 or 7-dimensions; with properly stated axioms some fascinating theorems emerge. They are true and valid within their context, but not in general relevant to this physical world, simply because it happens to occupy three spatial dimensions, not four or five. Nevertheless, to the mathematician, all are equally interesting and important.

In scientific inference, on the other hand, we are concerned almost exclusively with the extent to which our axioms (our 'model') correspond to the 'real' world. It is a process that will be found many times in the following chapters and in many guises, like the theme of a symphony or a concerto. In a way, it is the theme of this book. As such, it should be stated clearly and simply at the beginning in the hope that there will be a warmth of recognition when the reader encounters it again.

We can make no direct observations on the center of the earth. In the process of scientific inference and its application to some phenomenon in geophysics (say, the eruption of volcanoes), we first lay down certain axioms or statements, possibly on the nature of the material in this region or possibly on the motions involved. This is the *model*, the description of what we think may take place or may be there. The choice of the model is guided by a number of considerations. One, of course, is the phenomenon in which we are interested. We must include in our description as much as possible of what we think is relevant to the eruption of volcanoes, excluding what is not. Thus, we would be concerned with the temperature and pressure inside the earth, and not with the snowfall on the mountain. Another consideration is an appreciation of prior models with their successes and their limitations. Sometimes a model that has been a failure (in the sense described below) can be modified slightly to include something previously overlooked, and become a resounding success. Yet another is simplicity. A simple model, with an economy of hypothesis—that is, with as few and as simple new assumptions as possible—is more appealing aesthetically and if successful, is more definitive. There are fewer variables that can influence the result. Another is compatibility. If the model is to complement others which are believed to be successful, it should be compatible with them at the points of contact; it should be consistent with what we already know. Within these confines, however, the imagination can roam.

The formulation of this tentative model is the first step. The second involves its analysis. This part is purely deductive. The model is our set of axioms—what theorems can we prove? The more, of course, the better. For the theoretician, this step may involve intense hard work, in which the simplicity and economy of his model may be not merely an advantage but necessary if the mathematics is to get anywhere at all. Let us assume, however, that all goes well and that certain conclusions can be drawn from the model, certain properties found that were not obvious beforehand, certain 'predictions' made. Finally, these must then be compared with observations made on the earth itself, and the model judged on the basis of this comparison. If, in some respect, the model behaves as the earth does, then some element of credence is accorded the model—it may be regarded in that respect as an approximate representation of the earth itself. If the predictions of the model are found to be relevant to the earth in several or many respects (that is, if a number of phenomena are 'explained') then a greater credence is given to it; it may develop a capital letter and become a Theory. But there is never anything sacred about the model. If, despite many successes, even one prediction should be wildly in error, if it should fail to predict some observed property that it should, or predict something contrary to observation, then it must be revised or discarded without regret. It may be a minor revision or a qualification that is necessary, or the whole idea and description may be wrong.

Some models are intrinsically better than others. To require an elaborate set of new hypotheses to 'explain' (in this sense) one observation is worthless. One new hypothesis per prediction is no progress. A model which cannot give numerical prediction but merely qualitative indication is seriously deficient—we shall see examples of this later. One which enables apparently unrelated observations to be interpreted accurately in a common framework, without forcing, achieves a modest triumph. The more it can do this, the more excited we can become, and the more credence we accord it.

It is important, however, to remember always that we can never *prove* that any model is an accurate representation of the earth in certain specific respects. Even if a model gives twenty predictions of different observed quantities, all of which are successful and in accordance with measurements on the earth, there is no guarantee that this is the *only* model that will do so. Indeed, one of the plagues of certain parts of this subject is that almost any mildly sensible model will give about the same answers!

In this book, and in the mind of the working Geophysicist, the separation of these three steps involved in scientific inference is not always so distinct. He encounters an observation and wonders about its implication; his model is inspired by one kind of measurement and its success or failure depends on its relevance (or lack of it) to others. Bit by bit the pieces fit together and the pattern becomes more distinct. Sometimes mistakes will be made; we will think that part of the puzzle is done until we find a piece—a measurement or an observation—that will not fit in with what has gone before. Then there is no choice; that part must be done again. The puzzle is not finished; there are many pieces still not fitted in, and many gaps where there are no pieces at all. But after all, as with any puzzle, the pleasure comes not from the completed picture, but from the doing.

2

Gravitation and the
Figure of the Earth

2.1 THE SIZE OF THE EARTH

The simplest questions we can ask about any object are "How big is it?" and "How much does it weigh?" While in no way definitive, answers to these questions will give some indication about what is inside. Certain possibilities can be excluded immediately—if a small piece of painted wood is heavy, it is not balsa, and if a large object is light, it is not entirely made of lead.

The first of these two questions is the easier. As with many others, this story begins with the Greeks. Long before Magellan completed his circumnavigation, the Greeks knew that the earth is very nearly spherical; they even knew its radius quite accurately. They noticed that at a certain place on the Nile near Aswan, at noon on midsummer day, a plumb line hanging vertically cast no shadow. The sun was vertically upwards; the place lay on the Tropic of Cancer. On the same day at noon in Alexandria (which lies about 450 miles or 720 kilometers* to the north), however, this was not so; the plumb line did cast a short but distinct shadow to the north. The sun lay a little to the south of the vertical. The rays from the very distant sun are, for all purposes here, parallel, and the only interpretation of these observations seems to be that the verticals at the two places are themselves not quite parallel; that the surface of the earth is rounded. The situation is illustrated in Figure 1, from which we will show that some simple measurements, combined with a little geometry would enable us (as it did the Greeks) to infer the radius $\Re$ of the earth. The figure is not, of course, drawn to scale; the lengths of the plumb lines are exaggerated so that they can be seen. Suppose that l represents the length of the plumb line at Alexandria and s the length of the shadow which it casts at the instant that the sun is vertical at Aswan, a distance d ($= 450$ miles) to the south. The two plumb lines hang vertically down, and each points to the center of the earth.† In the figure, O is the point where the two verticals meet and this is the center of the earth. Let us draw a horizontal straight line through the point A at Alexandria; since the surface of the earth is curved, Aswan lies somewhat below the horizon as seen at Alexandria, and this straight line will arrive at Aswan a little distance (BC) above the earth's surface. Nevertheless, let the distance AC be represented by d'. Now, in Figure 1, there are two similar triangles; the one at Alexandria formed by the plumb line, its shadow and the sun's rays and the larger one formed by Alexandria itself (A), the center of the earth O and the point C. In a pair of similar triangles like this, the ratios of corresponding sides are equal:

$$s/l = d'/\Re,$$

so that, on multiplication of both sides of the equation by $\Re l/s$, we have

$$\Re = \frac{d'l}{s}. \tag{2.1}$$

---

* 1 kilometer is about 5/8 of a mile. A table of metric units and equivalents is given in Appendix 1.
† This is not *exactly* true, as we shall see later, but is very nearly so.

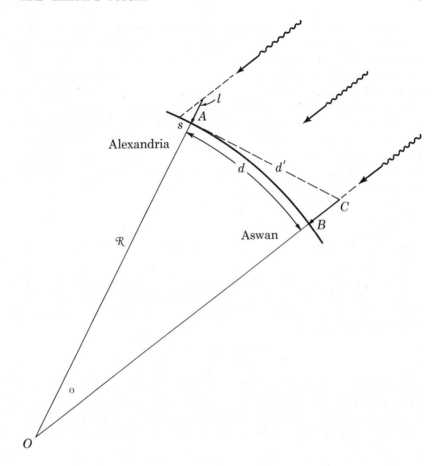

Figure 1. To find the radius of the earth, we can observe the length s of the shadow of a plumb line of
length l at Alexandria at an instant when, at Aswan,
the sun's rays are vertical. The point O, the intersection of the verticals at Alexandria and Aswan, is at the
center of the earth. d is the distance between the two
points measured along the surface and d' the straight
line distance in the direction of the horizon at Alexandria.

In this formula, the lengths l of the plumb line and s of its shadow at Alexandria can be measured easily; if we knew d' we could calculate the radius of the earth. Now the straight line distance d' is difficult to measure directly, but we can measure very simply the distance d between Alexandria and Aswan along the curved surface of the earth. It is apparent from the figure that, since the distance between the two points is only a small fraction of the radius of the earth, these two distances are very nearly equal;* we might then approximate the straight line distance d' in equation (2.1) by the more simply measured surface distance d. Consequently

$$\mathcal{R} \simeq \frac{dl}{s}, \tag{2.2}$$

where the $\simeq$ sign indicates a very close, though not exact equality.

Now, at noon on midsummer day at Alexandria, a plumb line of length $l = 100$ cm can be found by experiment to cast a shadow about 11.4 cm ($= s$) long. Therefore, $s/l = 0.114$. The distance d is 720 km, so that

$$\mathcal{R} \simeq \frac{720}{0.114} = 6400 \text{ km}, \tag{2.3}$$

or 4000 miles, nearly. In this way, a simple experiment and a little geometry has enabled us to measure the radius of the earth.

There is one thing further to notice about this experiment. It can be performed at noon on any day, not just at midsummer,

---

* In trigonometrical terms, $d'/\mathcal{R} = \tan\theta$, where θ (Greek theta) is the angle subtended by Alexandria and Aswan at the center of the earth, measured in radians. Also, the angle θ itself is defined, in radian measure, as the ratio of the *arc* length d to the radius $\mathcal{R}$. The exact relation between d and d' is therefore given by

$$d'/\mathcal{R} = \tan(d/\mathcal{R}).$$

When $d/\mathcal{R}$ is small, (i.e., when the distance between the two points is small compared with the radius of the earth), it is known from trigonometry that $\tan(d/\mathcal{R}) = d/\mathcal{R}$ very nearly, so that from the expression above $d' = d$. The error in (2.3) resulting from this approximation is less than 1%.

and at any two places on the surface of the earth which have an appreciable north-south separation, which we will still call d. If l_1 is the length of the plumb line furthest from the equator and s_1 the length of the shadow that it casts, while l_2 and s_2 are the corresponding lengths at the other point, it can be shown by geometry only a little different from that given above that the earth's radius ℜ is then given by

$$\Re = \frac{d}{\tan^{-1}(s_1/l_1) - \tan^{-1}(s_2/l_2)}, \qquad (2.4)$$

where $\tan^{-1}(s_1/l_1)$ means "the angle in radians whose tangent is (s_1/l_1)." The proof of this can be left as an exercise; it will be noted that if $s_2 = 0$ (as at Aswan in midsummer), this reduces to (2.2) since $\tan^{-1} 0 = 0$, and $\tan^{-1}(s_1/l_1) \simeq s_1/l_1$.

The answer that we have found, 6400 kilometers or 4000 miles, is very close to the actual radius of the earth. The volume of a sphere of radius ℜ is $(4/3)\pi\Re^3$, so that for the earth,

$$\text{Volume} = \tfrac{4}{3}\pi \times (6400)^3 = 1,100,000,000,000$$
$$\text{cubic kilometers, nearly,}$$
$$= 1.1 \times 10^{12} \text{ cubic km.} \qquad (2.5)$$

Measured in cubic miles, by a similar calculation,

$$\text{Volume} = 268,000,000,000 \text{ cubic miles,}$$
$$= 2.68 \times 10^{11} \text{ cubic miles.}$$

These are huge numbers and in themselves almost meaningless. We have no way of visualizing such numbers; no feeling for their magnitudes. It is difficult to conceive even one cubic mile, let alone hundreds of billions. Nonetheless, they are the end results of this part of the inquiry, and we shall return to them later. They are a step toward others that are literally pregnant with significance.

2.2 THE IDEAS OF MASS AND WEIGHT

The first of our questions has been answered, at least to a reasonable approximation. The search for the second answer will lead us far. We shall look up, to the motions of the planets and their satellites. We shall follow the greatest minds of the Scientific Renaissance in their quest for order and simplicity in the nature of the material world. We shall find the keystone in an improbable experiment devised by an 18th century amateur scientist—an experiment which nevertheless worked.

We shall even find that the question as asked is meaningless. In the seeking of the answer, the first step is to find the right question.

What is meant by 'weight'? The primitive concept is derived from the effort required to lift something; we can say that the weight of an object is the force with which it is attracted to the earth. This indeed can be taken as our definition; the word 'weight' will be taken to mean this, no more and no less. It is measured by a spring balance. As shown in Figure 2, the weight W is the force that stretches the spring to give the reading on the scale. An important thing about the weight of a given object is that it is *not* always the same. If the object is carried to different places on the surface of the earth, it is found that the gravi-

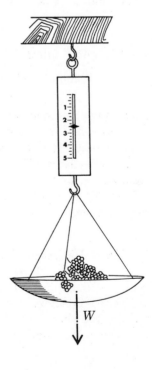

Figure 2. A spring balance is used to measure *weight,* the force of attraction of an object toward the earth.

tational attraction varies a little, and consequently so does its weight. The main variation is, in fact, between the equator and the poles; it is not very large (amounting to about 1/2 of one per cent at most) but it is both definite and, as we shall see later, important. If the object is carried in a falling elevator, its weight apparently decreases. If it is in a spaceship, fired by a rocket into orbit, it will float quite freely around the cabin and its weight is apparently nothing. It is clear that weight is a property, not of the object alone, but also of where it is.

The idea of mass is quite distinct. It is concerned with the inertia, the amount of matter in a body, which is the same no matter where it is. Masses are compared and measured by banging two objects together in some arrangement like the double swing shown in Figure 3. Two cylinders are suspended horizontally and the lengths of the cords are adjusted so that they can collide end to end. Let us suppose that the cylinders are released in such a way that they are traveling at the same speed toward each other just before the collision. Moreover, suppose that the impact ends are sticky, so that there is no rebound. The masses of the two cylinders are said to be equal if both come immediately to a dead stop as a result of the collision. If, after the impact, cylinder No. 1 is still moving forward and No. 2 backwards, then 1 is more massive than 2; the mass m_1 is greater than m_2.

It is most important that the ideas of mass and weight be kept clear and distinct. We must be careful, since in common usage the terms are sometimes taken as synonymous, and to help confound confusion, they are both frequently measured in pounds or kilograms. But:

When a bus and a mini-car collide head-on, the bus forces the car back, not because it is heavier (i.e., has greater weight) but because it is more massive.

A blimp flies not because it has no mass, but because it has no *net* weight in the atmosphere; its buoyancy just balances the weight of all the parts that make up the blimp.

An astronaut landing on the moon, will have (one hopes) the same mass as he had when he left the earth, but consider-

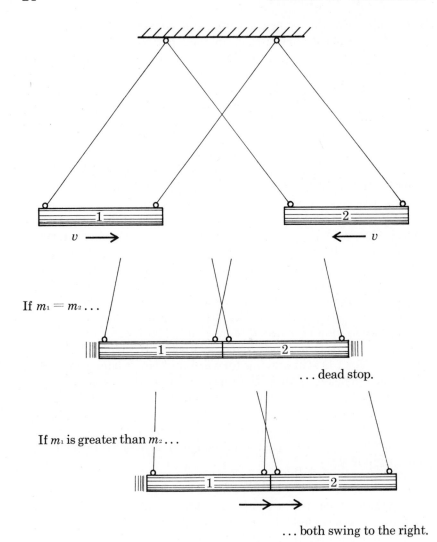

If $m_1 = m_2$ ...

... dead stop.

If m_1 is greater than m_2 ...

... both swing to the right.

Figure 3. A simple arrangement for comparing masses. The cylinders, moving at the same speed in opposite directions, collide and stick. If their masses are equal, they will both come to a dead stop. If cylinder #1 is more massive than #2, it will carry the latter backwards after the collision.

ably less weight, because the gravitational attraction on the surface of the moon is very much less than it is on earth.

A huge man is both heavy and massive. H. G. Wells' story "The Trouble with Pyecroft" tells of a fat man who wanted to lose *weight*. With the aid of a mysterious and secret medicine, he does so, but without losing *mass*. At the end of the story, he is as fat as ever, but floats about the ceiling like an enormous balloon.

Mass is measured in pounds or kilograms. These are units of mass, not of weight. Nevertheless, a body with a mass of one pound is commonly said to weigh one pound; the force of gravitational attraction between this body and the earth is called 'one pound.' This, as we have seen, varies from one place to another on the earth; to retain a distinction, as we must, the force will be called *one pound weight;* the weight of a body with a mass of one kilogram is *one kilogram weight*.

Although mass, being intrinsic to a body, is apparently a more fundamental property than weight, the weight of objects will ultimately concern us just as much. The latter arises from some kind of interaction between bodies and the earth itself, and the exploration of this interaction, which we call gravity, will provide us with important clues in our search.

Two last points should be made. First, since at any location on the surface of the earth, mass is proportional to weight, it follows that masses can be compared more conveniently by means of a beam balance. The chemist's balance (Figure 4) is a common type. Although impact experiments are fundamental in establishing the idea of mass, they are hardly practical as a means of routine measurement, so that for this, a beam balance is always used. Secondly, it is time to return to the second of the questions posed at the beginning of the chapter: "What is the weight of the earth?" It now appears that the question has no meaning. Since we have insisted that the weight of an object is its gravitational attraction to the earth, how can this apply to the earth itself? What we must seek is not the weight of the earth, but its mass. In recognizing the need to rephrase the question, we are a step toward finding the answer.

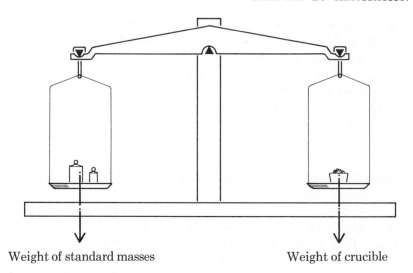

Weight of standard masses   Weight of crucible

Figure 4. A chemical balance. When the lever is balanced, the weights of the objects in the two pans are
equal. Since weight is proportional to mass, the masses
in each pan are also equal.

2.3 FORCE AND THE BEGINNINGS OF MECHANICS

We do not know *why* there is a gravitational attraction toward the earth; this most profound question is still unanswered.
But it is possible to find out *how* this attraction behaves, and
what its properties are. To do this, we must consider the ob-
servables, the motions of bodies under the influence of gravity
and this leads back to the laws of motion themselves.

Mechanics is the science of motion. It is based on three laws,
or summaries of physical experience that were enunciated by
Isaac Newton in his *Principia Mathematica*, published in 1687.
He called them axioms of motion, regarding them as the foundations of a deductive theory of mechanics in the sense that was
described previously. From our viewpoint, though, they should
more properly be regarded as the elements of a model, whose

success is evident from the manifold correspondences between predictions based upon them and observations of physical 'reality.' So striking has been their success that these laws were believed, until the end of the last century, to represent the ultimate statement of the laws governing the motion of the universe.

Today, however, we should be more modest; they have been found to fail in two extremes—when the dimensions involved approach the size of an atom and when the speeds approach the speed of light. The modifications of Newton's laws in these contexts are the domain of quantum theory and relativity respectively, but fortunately, neither of the limits will concern us here. For the purposes that we require, Newton's laws can be regarded as statements of remarkable accuracy and generality; a framework in which we can interpret the motions of marbles, of mountains, of the planets and the stars themselves.

Newton stated his first law as follows: "Every body continues in its state of rest, or of uniform motion in a straight line, unless compelled to change that state by impressed forces." * This is a statement of what is regarded as the natural condition of things. If a body is at rest, it remains at rest unless pushed; if it is sliding, it will continue to do so at the same speed and in the same direction unless there is some 'force' acting upon it to retard or deflect it. The operation of this law is all too evident to the driver of a car skidding on ice. Nevertheless, the statement represents an abstraction, an idealization of nature. The car will ultimately stop, even though it remains on ice; even a skater cannot glide forever. To account for this, we must insist that there is some retarding influence, a little force of friction between the tires and the ice. The qualification is always invoked —things never move exactly at constant speed in a straight line, so that some forces must always be acting. The word 'force' here must still be interpreted in its primitive sense—as something which can be felt by muscular effort. The idea is still woolly, but the meaning that we shall ascribe to the word is made precise by the second law.

---

* From Motte's translation of *Principia* (1729) reprinted by University of California Press, Berkeley, California, 1946.

This is, again in Motte's translation of Newton's words, that "the change of motion is proportional to the motive force impressed, and is made in the direction of the right line in which that force is impressed."

This law, like those of Congress, will have to be interpreted. "The change of motion" means, not just the change of velocity but the rate of change of velocity, the acceleration. The greater the acceleration a the greater the motive force F required; the two moreover are asserted to be in direct proportion. This can be stated symbolically: for a given body

$$F \propto a, \tag{2.6}$$

where the $\propto$ sign means "is proportional to."

The *directions* of the force and acceleration are important; if the force acts in a certain direction, then the body accelerates in this direction. If a body is already moving and a force acts to retard the motion, the direction of the force is opposite to that of the velocity. If we assign a positive sign to the direction of the motion, then the force is negative, and consequently the acceleration is negative; the body decelerates. Moreover, there is no requirement that the force at any instant act along the same line as the velocity at that instant. The idea of velocity involves both speed and direction; if either the speed or the direction of a body changes, an acceleration (and so a force) is involved. For example, if a stone on a string is whirled around your head, its speed remains the same but the direction of motion changes constantly; it is continually accelerating *inwards* so that it remains on its circular path. A force is required to produce this, a force that is felt as the pull on the string. If the string is suddenly released, the force on the stone ceases and it flies off, initially on a straight line. Once it is flying 'free,' we have a rather different situation but again one that involves forces and accelerations. The only forces acting then are its weight and the resistance of the air; neglecting the latter for the moment, it can be seen that the force of gravity acts downwards and produces an acceleration in this direction. The stone begins to move downwards more and more rapidly until it strikes the ground.

Another example is to be found when children ride in the back of a station wagon as it rounds a bend of the road. As with the whirling stone, the car has an acceleration perpendicular to the direction of motion. If the children are relaxed, they will roll outwards, since, in the absence of any sideways force, they will tend to continue along the original straight line of the car's motion. They will be prevented from doing this only if they push against the floor or the walls of the car, forcing themselves to accelerate inwards with the rest of the vehicle. When the car brakes in a straight line, the speed (but not now the direction) changes, the whole car having an acceleration that is *opposite* the direction of motion. The children will tend to roll forward, maintaining a constant velocity, until they push themselves back to give their bodies the same negative acceleration as the car.

For a given body, force is proportional to acceleration: $F \propto a$. An equivalent statement is that force equals some constant times acceleration, or

$$F = ka, \tag{2.7}$$

where k is a basic characteristic of the body, a measure of its mass or inertia. The greater the inertia, the greater k and the greater the force required for a given acceleration. But it was established in the previous section that the mass of a body is the measure of its inertia; moreover it is the only such measure that we know. Is it possible to identify the constant of proportionality k with the mass m? The proper resolution of this question would lead us rather far afield, and it will not be attempted here. Suffice it to say that it is possible, that Newton's second law can be written in the form

$$F = ma, \tag{2.8}$$

one of the basic equations of mechanics, where m (mass) is now the constant in the previous equation.

It is possible and fruitful to regard this equation in another light. The mass has been defined previously and experiments devised from which it can be measured. The acceleration can be found by measuring the way in which the velocity of an object changes. But 'force' is still a primitive concept. This equation can be used, therefore, to *define* force: if a mass m experiences an acceleration a, we can say that a net force $F = ma$ must be

acting. This new, more precise meaning to the word is what we
shall use henceforth; fortunately, as we shall see, it represents
a clarification of the primitive idea rather than a new meaning.
One other thing is also now clear. The first law can be interpreted as a special case of the second. If a body in motion has
no forces acting on it, then in equation (2.8), $F = 0$. The mass
of the body is not zero, so that the only possibility allowed by the
equation is that $a = 0$; there is no acceleration. The body continues to move in a straight line at constant velocity, precisely
as stated by the first law.

The third of Newton's laws was stated as follows: "To every
action there is always opposed an equal reaction, or, the mutual
actions of two bodies upon each other are always equal and
directed to contrary parts." Here, there are two alternative
statements of the same idea. The first form has been invoked in
many contexts, from religion to economics (even to the point of
absurdity), but the second leaves little room to doubt that Newton was thinking only in terms of mechanics. As a statement, it
is perhaps not as clear as the other two laws; possibly Newton,
aware of this, offered the alternatives. The idea and its application are, however, quite clear. I hold a bottle of ink in my hand.
It is at rest; there is no acceleration a, so that from equation
(2.8), no *net* force. But there are separate and identifiable forces
on the bottle—its weight acting downwards and the force sup-
plied by my hand holding it up. But since there can be no net
force, these must exactly balance. The two are "equal and
directed to contrary parts." Again, in whirling the stone attached to a string about my head, I feel in my hand the force required to maintain the circular motion. The motion of the stone
pulls outwards on my hand; I must resist the pull with an equal
and opposite force inwards. Once more, action and reaction
balance. A final example: the moon is held in orbit about the
earth by means of, as we shall see shortly, the gravitational attraction of the earth. The earth applies a force to the moon that
is analogous in this respect to the inwards force I apply to the
whirling stone by means of the string. Just as the stone applies
an equal and opposite force outwards to my hand, so does the
moon produce an equal and opposite force on the earth, accord-

ing to this third law, a force which incidentally produces a greater part of the tidal activity of the earth's oceans.

Contained in these three laws are the foundations of mechanics, except for the very small and for the very fast. One can criticize the logical arrangement of the laws, their degree of independence and mutual consistency but, though interesting and important, this would represent a digression from our main theme. It is more immediately relevant to consider how these laws can be used to interpret the motions that we observe, and thence the forces which must ultimately be associated with the material inside the earth.

To this end, let us consider a body of mass m, freely falling under gravity, supposing for the moment that the air resistance is negligible. The only force acting is the weight, W. If W is substituted for F in the equation of motion, $F = ma$, it follows that the acceleration downwards of the falling body is

$$a = W/m,$$

which, at a particular point on the earth's surface is a constant, and independent of the mass of the body. The fact that different freely falling bodies move with constant acceleration was, indeed, established experimentally by Galileo in 1638. This experiment is important in demonstrating the proportionality between weight and mass (which we have implicitly assumed earlier) and also because it indicates how close was Galileo to the ideas of force, weight, mass and inertia—ideas which still had to wait fifty years for Newton.

The acceleration due to gravity is customarily denoted by g, so that the weight and mass of a body are related by

$$W = mg. \tag{2.9}$$

Now, the weight of a particular body is not quite the same at different points on the surface of the earth, even though its mass is invariant; its gravitational attraction to the earth varies somewhat. It is evident from the previous equation that the variations in weight are exactly equivalent to variations in the gravitational acceleration g. This is, in fact, a more fundamental

quantity to consider, since the weight of a body is a property of
the body (through its mass) and of its location, whereas the
gravitational acceleration g depends on the location only, being
independent of the mass as Galileo's experiment demonstrated.
The acceleration g can, of course, be found from free fall experiments, but although this is the simplest in principle, it is
not the most convenient way. We are interested, not only in the
average magnitude of g, but also in the small variations from
place to place, since this information contains evidence (which
we will still have to unravel) of the variations in structure of
the earth beneath us. The measurements must be made to considerable accuracy, therefore, and it is difficult in free fall experiments to insure that extraneous effects like air resistance
do not influence the results. There are alternatives, however.
One can carry a given mass about on the earth's surface and
measure (with a spring balance) the small variations in its
weight. A gravimeter is an instrument which, in essence, does
this. Alternatively, one can measure g by means of a pendulum.
A simple pendulum consists of a concentrated mass m hanging
at the end of a light string of length l. Now, set the pendulum
in motion. It can be found by simple observation (or shown
theoretically from Newton's laws, as in Appendix 2) that no
matter how little or how far (within limits) the pendulum
swings, it always takes the same time T to perform a single
cycle. To say the same thing a little more precisely: if the
amplitude of the oscillation (the maximum angle of the string
to the vertical, at the end of its swing) is sufficiently small, then
the periodic time T is independent of this amplitude. But if we
change the mass m of the bob, or the length l of the string or
the location (and so the gravitational acceleration g), then T
may change, though even under these new conditions, it will be
independent of the amplitude of the swing. The precise way in
which T depends on these quantities, m, l, and g, can be found by
setting up a differential equation for the motion (Appendix 2)
or, more simply, by dimensional analysis.

The period T is measured in seconds, the length l (in metric
units) in centimeters, the mass m in grams and g, an acceleration or a change in velocity per unit time in (centimeters per

second) per second, or cm sec^{-2}.* Now, the periodic time T must be given by some combination of l, m and g.

$$T = \text{some function of } l, m, g, \tag{2.10}$$

and whatever combination it is it must have the 'physical dimensions' of seconds. An equation can balance only if it equates like quantities. But m is measured in grams, and if it entered the equation it would necessarily be unbalanced, since it is the only one of the variables in which 'grams' enter. There are no 'grams' on the left hand side of equation (2.10) so that there can be none on the right either. We therefore reach the immediate (and perhaps surprising) conclusion that T does *not* depend on the mass m after all; the periodic time is independent of the mass of the bob! Consequently, equation (2.10) can be simplified to

$$T = \text{some function of } l \text{ and } g; \tag{2.11}$$

the task is now to discover *what* function.

The dimension 'centimeters' can be canceled out by taking the combination

$$[g/l] = \frac{\text{cm sec}^{-2}}{\text{cm}} = \text{sec}^{-2},$$

where the square brackets indicate that we are interested in the dimensions or units of the quantity contained inside. Inversion of both sides of this equation gives

$$[l/g] = \text{sec}^2,$$

and taking the square root, we have

$$[(l/g)^{1/2}] = \text{sec}.$$

This is the only possible combination of l and g that will give the same dimensions as T. We can therefore assert that, since T is determined by these quantities alone, then T must necessarily be proportional to this combination:

$$T = A(l/g)^{1/2}, \tag{2.12}$$

---

* Centimeters per second can be written briefly as cm/sec, or, borrowing the index notation from ordinary arithmetic, as cm sec^{-1}. Correspondingly, (centimeters per second) per second can be written (cm/sec)/sec, or cm/sec^2, or cm sec^{-2}.

where A is a pure number.* This technique of dimensional analysis has very wide applicability in physical problems, and there will be opportunity to use it again later. Its advantage is that it does not depend on a detailed analysis of the motion involved (that is, on a mathematical development of Newton's laws) but only on a careful consideration of the parameters or physical quantities involved. Its disadvantage is that it provides no information about any dimensionless numbers, in this case A. For this, a detailed analysis such as that of Appendix 2 *is* necessary, where it is found that $A = 2\pi$. As a result, then,

$$T = 2\pi(l/g)^{1/2}, \tag{2.13}$$

our final expression for the period of a simple pendulum in terms of its length l and the acceleration g due to gravity.

If we square both sides of this equation,

$$T^2 = 4\pi^2 \frac{l}{g},$$

and then multiply throughout by g and divide by T^2, we have

$$g = \frac{4\pi^2 l}{T^2}, \tag{2.14}$$

a solution for g in terms of l and T. The simple pendulum, then, offers a fine way of measuring g, since l and T can be found to great accuracy.

The average value of g found in this way is about 980 cm/sec², with variations ranging from 978.0 near the equator to 983.0 near the poles.

Another important application of Newton's laws is to circular motion, and the results that we will now derive will be used in several contexts later. The argument is a little intricate but important. Suppose a particle or small body of mass m is moving with constant *speed* v in a circle of radius R, say a stone being whirled around one's head. What is the force acting on the body in the inward radial direction to maintain the motion? Newton's second law gives this directly in terms of the acceleration, so

* like 2 or 75; not two bananas or two grams but just two.

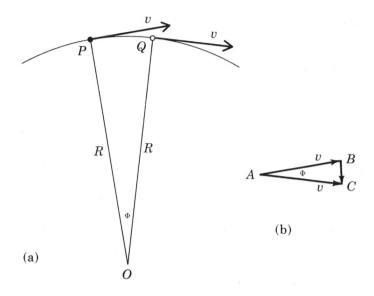

Figure 5. A body moves in circular motion about O with a constant speed v. At one instant it is at P; a short time δt later at Q. The arrows marked at P and Q represent the magnitude and direction of the velocities at these points; they are redrawn in (b). The length BC then represents the *change* in velocity over the short time interval δt.

that the real problem is to find this acceleration. The situation is illustrated in Figure 5(a). Suppose that at one instant, the particle is at P while a very short time δt later it is at Q.* The small angle subtended by the arc PQ at the center O of the circle will be called Φ (Greek phi). Now, the speed at Q is the same as the speed at P, but the direction of motion is different; if we draw a little triangle ABC (Figure 5(b)) so that AB represents the *velocity* at P (its length representing the speed and its direction, the direction of motion at P) while AC repre-

---

* The combination δt is to be regarded as a single symbol, δ (Greek delta) being understood as 'a small change in,' so that δt means 'a small change in the time' or 'a small time interval.'

sents the corresponding velocity at Q, then BC represents the *change* in velocity of the particle between P and Q. Moreover, the angle BAC is the same as the angle between the two tangents at P and Q of Figure 5(a) ; this in turn is equal to the angle PAQ subtended by the points P and Q, the angle that we have called Φ.

Now, remember that the body is moving at constant speed around the circle, so that the *lengths* of the lines AB and AC, representing the speeds at P and Q, are the same. The velocities, however, are different, since the directions of motion are different, and *the line BC represents in its length and direction the magnitude and direction of the change in velocity that has occurred in the small time interval δt*. Since the angle Φ is very small, the direction of BC is very nearly perpendicular to AC (or AB), that is, perpendicular to the direction of motion at P. The change in the velocity in the interval δt is therefore in the inwards radial direction and since the acceleration is just this change divided by the time interval δt, then it also is directed *inwards along the radius*. This, at least, confirms what we already know from experience, from the fact that we must pull inwards along a radius in order to keep a whirling stone in its circular path.

The remaining question is this: what is the magnitude of the acceleration a? This is defined generally as

$$a = \frac{\text{change in velocity in time interval } \delta t}{\delta t},$$

or in our case

$$a = \frac{\text{velocity represented by the length } BC}{\delta t}. \qquad (2.15)$$

Now this length BC is indistinguishable, in Figure 5(b), from the length of the arc BC of a circle whose center is at A; let us imagine the figure to represent such a sector and compare it with the sector OPQ. Evidently, since the angles Φ marked are the same, these two sectors are similar (in the same sense that triangles are similar) and the ratios of corresponding sides are the same. So

$$\frac{\text{Arc length } PQ}{\text{radius } R} = \frac{\text{`Arc length' } BC}{\text{`radius' } v}.$$

But the arc length PQ is just the distance the body has moved at speed v during the interval δt, or $v\,\delta t$, so that

$$\frac{v\,\delta t}{R} = \frac{\text{velocity change represented by } BC}{v}.$$

If we now multiply both sides of the equation by v, the change in velocity that occurs in the time interval δt (represented by BC) is found to be

$$\frac{v^2}{R}\,\delta t,$$

so that from (2.15), the acceleration in a circular motion with radius R and speed v is given by

$$a = \frac{v^2}{R}, \tag{2.16}$$

directed along the inwards radius. Finally, then, the force required to maintain the motion is

$$F = ma = mv^2/R,$$

from Newton's second law. This is the force that we apply to the string attached to the whirling stone, the force that the earth must apply to the moon to keep it in its constant orbit.

2.4 KEPLER'S EMPIRICAL LAWS

The early history of celestial mechanics is a fascinating one, involving an interplay between observation, hypothesis and theology. Its ramifications cannot be traced here but five names are of enduring importance. It was Ptolemy (c. second century A.D.) who first formulated a mechanical model of the universe using ideas described earlier but less precisely by Aristotle (384–332 B.C.) —a rather complicated model with the earth at the center, the sun and moon circling around it, the other planets performing gyrations of circles upon circles and the distant stars beyond.* The authority of Aristotle's name was a stum-

---

* Ptolemy also considered very seriously a model with the sun at the center, but, on balance, decided to discard it.

bling block to alternative (and simpler) descriptions, and it was not until 1530 that Copernicus, a Pole, proposed again that the sun may be the center of the system with the other planets circling about it. This alternative, although simpler, aroused much opposition, and the competition between the two provoked a debate that was to arouse passions and was to consume, not just emotional energy but almost literally, the person of Galileo himself. Although he did not accept Copernicus' description, the Danish astronomer Tycho Brahe (1546–1601) over his lifetime amassed great volumes of observational data on the motion of the planets known in his day. These were to provide Johannes Kepler (1571–1631), his student, with the raw material from which, by tireless calculation, he distilled three 'laws' or empirical statements which he found to govern the motion of these planets. The further refinement into one single law of gravitation had to await the genius of Newton and the understanding of mechanics that he gave.

The elements of this achievement, involving a synthesis of observation, deduction, and inference are in many respects an archetype of the ways in which more complex geophysical models are built. As such, they are worth following in some detail so that we may appreciate more clearly the same kind of development as it occurs in other parts of our inquiry.

Let us begin with the empirical laws that Kepler found could summarize the mass of Brahe's data. He found that:

(i) Every planet traces out an ellipse with the sun at one focus.

An ellipse is one of the classical figures of Euclidean geometry. It can be traced mechanically in the following way. Imagine two pegs at points F_1 and F_2 in Figure 6 with a loop of string placed loosely over them. If a pencil is placed in the loop and moved outwards until the string is taut, the figure that it traces out as it moves around the two pegs is an ellipse. The points F_1 and F_2 are known as the *foci*, and the geometrical center O is midway between them. If the loop around the pegs has only a little slack, the ellipse is very flattened; if it is longer, the ellipse is more full, more nearly circular. A limiting case is worth noting: if the positions of the two pegs should coincide, then the loop constrains the pencil to a fixed distance so that it traces out a circle. An ellipse with coincident foci is simply a circle. The ellipticity (degree of flattening) of the planetary orbits is much less than is illustrated in Figure 6; the greatest and least

Figure 6. The tracing of an ellipse.

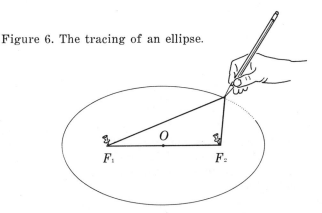

diameters generally differ by only a few per cent and the paths are very nearly circular. Nevertheless, the accuracy of the astronomical observations was sufficient to detect this difference and to demonstrate that the sun does lie at a focus and not (say) at the geometrical center.

Secondly, Kepler found that:

(ii) Every planet moves in such a way that the rate at which area is swept out by its radius vector to the sun is the same for all parts of the orbit.

This law is illustrated in Figure 7. The radius vector is the line joining the center of the planet to the center of the sun; as the planet moves, it sweeps out the area of the ellipse. Kepler's second law states that for any planet, the rate at which this happens is the same over the entire orbit, no matter how eccentric (elongated) the ellipse. So, in Figure 7, suppose that P is the position of a planet at one instant and Q its position a week later; several months afterwards, the planet is at P' and a week after that, at Q'. This statement asserts that the areas PSQ and $P'SQ'$ are the same. If the radius vector PS is shorter than

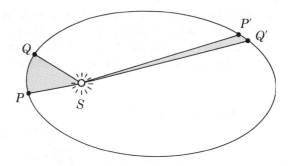

Figure 7. During a certain interval of time, a planet
moves in its orbit from P to Q. In another part of its
orbit, during an equal interval of time, it moves from
P' to Q'. Kepler's second law states that the shaded
areas are the same, no matter where the points P and
P' lie on the orbit.

$P'S$, the planet must be moving faster at P than at P' if equal
areas are to be swept out.

Finally:

(iii) For all planets, the square of the period of revolution
about the sun T divided by the cube of the average
distance d from the sun, is the same.

$$T^2/d^3 = \text{constant for } all \text{ planets.}$$

This is, in some ways, a strange law. It could be merely an odd
fact, a coincidence of nature. Its significance is far from obvious,
yet, as we shall see, it contains within it a direct clue to the law
of gravitation.

These were the statements that faced Newton,* the primary
observational criteria against which any model of the plane-

---

* Later, more accurate measurements have shown very small departures from these laws of Kepler. These can be interpreted as the result
of gravitational interactions among the planets *themselves:* Kepler's
laws would hold exactly if the orbit of each planet was influenced only
by the sun. The small perturbations in the planetary orbits are discussed briefly in Section 2.6.

tary motions had to be judged. His laws of motion were established (not yet too firmly) ; what additional ingredients were
necessary in order to construct a dynamical model consistent
with them? It was to transpire that only one further hypothesis
was necessary in order that all should fall into place; and moreover only one form of the hypothesis would be allowable. Before
we follow in Newton's steps, however, let us pause to appreciate
the conceptual difficulties that he faced.

The first involved the applicability of his laws of motion. These
were derived from, and had been tested in experience with
small objects—on a 'laboratory scale.' Were the same laws ap-
plicable to the enormously larger scales represented by the motion of the planets? It required great daring to suppose that they
were, a supposition which, while not contradicted by experience,
was certainly as yet unsubstantiated. But even if this supposition were made, great difficulties remained. The planets do not
move in straight lines at constant velocity, so that presumably
there must be some forces to produce their acceleration. Perhaps
Newton argued by analogy with the whirling stone, but in this
case, the string is *attached* to the stone and held in the hand.
No strings attach the planets to the sun. How can a force be
transmitted across empty space, tying the earth to the sun, the
moon to the earth? It was obvious that forces could be transmitted by contact, by one body pushing directly against another,
but this seemed an entirely different conception.

Yet Newton cannot have been completely unaware of this kind
of phenomenon. He knew about magnets and how they influence
one another, even when not in contact. When cat's fur is rubbed
with amber, the fur will rise on end when the amber is brought
near; *why* the attraction takes place may have been mysterious,
but the *fact* that it does was well-known. This was evidently a
new kind of interaction between material bodies, one that was
labeled 'action at a distance.' Could the same sort of thing be
involved in the motion of the planets about the sun?

Today, our point of view is different. It has been found more
convenient to think of a body, such as the earth or the sun, being
surrounded by a gravitational *field,* a property of the space surrounding the body that is associated with the presence of the
body. When a second body, with its own gravitational field,

enters that of the earth, say, the interaction between the two
fields is manifest as a force of attraction between the bodies.
This concept of a field is useful in many contexts—one can talk
about electric fields, magnetic fields, nuclear fields as well as
gravitational fields, but it is important to remember that this
description brings us no closer to answering the question, "*Why*
is there a gravitational attraction?" This we cannot yet answer;
the idea of a field is a way of representing the fact that there is.

One other difficulty faced Newton, one of technique. Though
one of the foremost mathematicians of his day, Newton knew
little more mathematics than does a modern high school gradu-
ate, and this is not really sufficient to handle all the intricacies
of elliptical orbits. He was sufficiently perceptive, however, to
realize that, for a proper analysis of the problems posed, a new
kind of mathematics was necessary: a calculus of infinitesimals.
He was therefore forced to devise his own mathematics, to in-
vent what we now call differential calculus. About the same time,
but independently, Leibnitz in Germany was discovering the
need for the same kind of mathematics to solve quite different
problems; these two men are, by any measure, the fathers of
modern mathematics.

2.5 NEWTON: THE LAW OF GRAVITATION

The task facing us, as it did Newton, is to draw from Kepler's
laws a simpler relation (a model) concerning the gravitational
interaction between the planets and the sun. We shall find that
only one form of the interaction is possible, only one is consistent with these three observational statements.

Let us begin with Kepler's second law, the statement illustrated in Figure 7 about equal areas being swept out by the
radius vector in equal times. Now, it was mentioned earlier that
the ellipticities of many of the planetary orbits are small; they
are very nearly circular. Let us suppose for the moment that
they *are* circular, as illustrated in Figure 8; what can we infer
from Kepler's second law in this case? Since the path is circular
and since the rate at which area is swept out by the radius vector
is the same at all parts of the orbit, it follows that the *speed* of

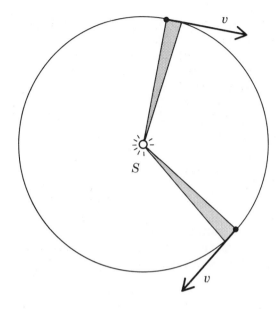

Figure 8. In a circular orbit, Kepler's second law implies that the speed of the planet is constant.

the planet is the same, no matter where it is in the trajectory.
In other words, the planet is in a circular orbit at constant speed,
the kind of motion considered at the end of Section 2.3. What, in
turn, does this imply? What does this tell us about the forces
acting on the planet as it moves? First of all, we know that there
must be an inwards force mv^2/R, necessary to keep it on its
circular path. This acts at right angles to the direction of motion,
and produces the constant turning associated with the circular
motion. But from Kepler's second law, we have inferred that
the *speed* of motion is constant; there is no acceleration or re-
tardation along the line of motion, and consequently, there can
be no force acting in this direction. In other words: *the only
force acting on the planet must be the radial one, directly toward the sun.* This is the physical content of Kepler's second law.

The argument above was based on the special case of a circular orbit. The interpretation of this law for an elliptical orbit
requires some calculus but the conclusion is the same: the force

of gravitational interaction between a planet and the sun is purely along the line of centers.

Let us now turn to the third law, to see what further inferences can be made from it. Again, we will approximate the elliptical orbit by circles. Kepler's third law, you will recall, asserts that the average distance d from the sun (or for circular orbits, the orbital radius R) and the time T that it takes for any planet to complete a circuit are such that

$$\frac{T^2}{R^3} = B, \text{ say, the same for all planets.} \qquad (2.17)$$

What information about the gravitational force is hidden in this relation?

The planets, we suppose, move in circular paths at constant speed,* and so experience a continual acceleration a inwards along the radius. This is given by equation (2.16) as

$$a = v^2/R,$$

so that from Newton's second law of motion, the attractive force on the planet is

$$F = m_p a = m_p v^2/R, \qquad (2.18)$$

where m_p represents the mass of the planet.

But the time T that it takes the planet to complete one circuit about the sun is the path length $2\pi R$ divided by the speed:

$$T = \frac{2\pi R}{v}$$

so that

$$v = \frac{2\pi R}{T},$$

and, on substitution in (2.18),

$$F = \frac{m_p}{R}\left(\frac{2\pi R}{T}\right)^2 = \frac{4\pi^2 m_p R}{T^2}. \qquad (2.19)$$

---

* not *velocity*, since the direction of motion is changing continually, and constant velocity would imply constancy of both speed and direction.

Now equation (2.17)—Kepler's third law—asserts that

$$T^2 = BR^3,$$

so that when this is substituted into (2.19),

$$F = \frac{4\pi^2 m_p R}{BR^3} = \left(\frac{4\pi^2}{B}\right) \frac{m_p}{R^2}. \tag{2.20}$$

Remember that B is the same for all planets, so that the term in brackets represents a rather uninteresting constant; the heart of the matter is expressed more clearly by the proportionality statement

$$F \propto m_p/R^2. \tag{2.21}$$

From Kepler's third law, we have deduced that the gravitational attraction between a planet and the sun is proportional to the mass of the planet and *inversely proportional to the square of the distance between them.* A planet at twice the distance experiences one-quarter the force per unit mass; at three times the distance the force is reduced to one-ninth. The steps in the argument have been deductive; if we grant Kepler's third law, no other manner of variation with distance is possible.

The reasoning can be taken a little further. There seems no reason why equation (2.21) should hold only for planets and only at the particular radii R at which they happen to orbit about the sun. A meteorite or a spacecraft of mass m_1 at *any* distance r from the sun is influenced by the sun's gravitational field; it will experience a force of the same nature. In general, then, we can express the force experiencd by *any* mass m_1 at *any* distance from the sun as

$$F \propto \frac{m_1}{r^2}.$$

This, remember, is the force on the mass m_1 produced by the attraction of the sun; by the action-reaction principle, there will be an equal and opposite force produced *on* the sun by the mass m_1. (In the whirling stone experiment, this is the force that the stone exerts on your hand.) But if the force *on* the mass m_1 is proportional to m_1, then the force on the sun is proportional to the mass of the sun, m_2, say. In other words the force of gravitational interaction must be proportional to both m_1 and m_2 (and inversely to the square of the distance between them), so that

$$F \propto \frac{m_1 m_2}{r^2}. \tag{2.22}$$

If we write the constant of proportionality in the equation as G, we have

$$F = G \frac{m_1 m_2}{r^2}. \tag{2.23}$$

This is our final form of Newton's law of gravitation. The constant G, the gravitational constant, is one of the fundamental physical properties of nature—it is for us the end of this road. Like the velocity of light and like Planck's constant in quantum theory, we do not know how to express G in terms of anything more 'fundamental.' Its existence and magnitude must be regarded as one of the basic properties of the world about us; unlike the mathematical constants (the pure numbers π for example), its value cannot be calculated but must be found by experiment.

What of Kepler's first law—that the orbits are elliptical with the sun at one focus? Does this contain any further information beyond what we have already adduced from the other two? The answer, in fact, is no; the inverse square law (2.23) is sufficient to guarantee that all closed planetary orbits are elliptical with the sun at a focus. This can be *deduced* from equation (2.23) but the steps involve a working knowledge of celestial mechanics and of the calculus that Newton had to devise; they will not be attempted here. We can, if we wish, regard Kepler's first law as valuable supporting evidence of the law of gravitation that we have found: the mathematical model represented by (2.23) allows a *prediction* about the possible shapes of the orbits, one that is in accord with Kepler's observational statement.

Many other predictions can be made by a combination of the laws of motion and gravitation, some of which we will explore. One might be mentioned briefly here. With an inverse square law of attraction, it can be shown that all *closed* orbits are elliptical, but that parabolic and hyperbolic orbits are also possible, as illustrated in Figure 9. In these, a body comes in from a great distance, turns around the sun and recedes again in a

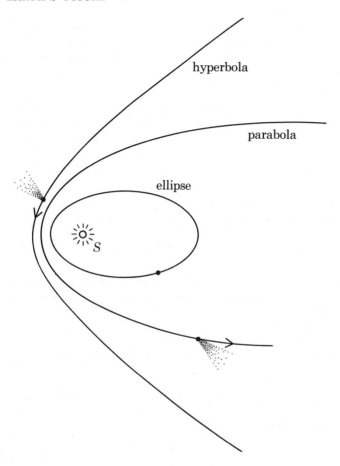

Figure 9. The three types of orbit possible with a Newtonian inverse square law of gravitation. Closed planetary orbits are elliptic (or circular). The orbits followed by some comets, which come from a great distance for a single encounter with the sun, are either hyperbolic or parabolic. In a hyperbola, the path is almost a straight line far from the sun; in a parabola, the path always curves, but ever more gently as the distance from the sun increases. (Note that the tail of a comet always points away from the sun, however it is moving.)

different direction. These alternatives were subsequently found to be of more than hypothetical interest; certain comets follow such paths, coming into the sun from interstellar space, enjoying a brief encounter and departing, never to return.

An important consequence of the law (2.23) of gravitation is the existence of a relation between the gravitational acceleration g at the surface of the earth on the one hand, and the mass and radius of the earth on the other. A body with mass m_1 at the surface of the earth has a gravitational attraction—its weight —toward the center of the earth, given by (2.23). The mass m_2 to which it is drawn is the mass of the earth, m_e say, while the distance r between the body and the center of the earth is $\Re$, the radius of the earth. The equation can then be transcribed as

$$F = G \frac{m_1 m_e}{\Re^2}.$$

Moreover, this force, the weight of the body, was shown in Section 2.3 to be expressible in terms of its mass and the acceleration due to gravity.

$$F = m_1 g.$$

These two equations express the same force, so that they can be equated:

$$m_1 g = G \frac{m_1 m_e}{\Re^2}.$$

Division by m_1 gives

$$g = G \frac{m_e}{\Re^2}. \tag{2.24}$$

It is evident that the mass m_1 has disappeared from the equation —the gravitational acceleration is independent of m_1, as indeed Galileo observed many years ago. This relation, however, tells much more: if we multiply both sides by $\Re^2$ and divide by G we have

$$\frac{g\Re^2}{G} = m_e.$$

We know the gravitational acceleration g and the radius of the earth $\Re$; if we could only find the gravitational constant G, we could calculate the mass of the earth! This, the object of our present search, seems deceptively close, but we are not quite there yet.

The discovery of the laws of motion and gravitation represented the triumph of 17th century science. They enabled astronomers to calculate the course of the planets, not only in the past, but years ahead; to do it with an accuracy never before known and even today unsurpassed in many branches of science. They could predict with confidence that years ahead, on a certain day and at a certain time, there would be an eclipse of the sun or of the moon. These laws are used today to work out the paths of satellites and spaceships as they travel to distant planets. With the simplest of algebra, we ourselves can deduce some interesting and important results on the motions of planets and satellites, results which bring us closer to our goal—the determination of the mass of the earth.

2.6 SATELLITES AND PLANETS

The previous results allow us to express the constant B in Kepler's third law (2.17) in terms of the gravitational constant G and the mass m_s of the sun. The law (2.23) of gravitation can be applied, of course, to the motion of a planet of mass $m_1 = m_p$ about the sun, of mass $m_2 = m_s$. Then r is the radius of the planetary orbit, which we have represented as R, so that the force of gravitational attraction is

$$F = G \frac{m_s m_p}{R^2}. \tag{2.25}$$

An alternative representation of this same force is given by (2.19) in terms of the orbit time T:

$$F = \frac{4\pi^2 m_p R}{T^2}.$$

These two can be equated.

$$\frac{4\pi^2 m_p R}{T^2} = G \frac{m_s m_p}{R^2}.$$

When both sides of this equation are divided by the product $G m_s m_p R$, there results

$$\frac{4\pi^2}{Gm_s T^2} = \frac{1}{R^3},$$

whence, after multiplication by T^2,

$$\frac{4\pi^2}{Gm_s} = \frac{T^2}{R^3}. \tag{2.26}$$

But the right hand side of this equation is precisely the same as the left of our original statement of Kepler's third law (2.17), so that the other sides must also be the same.

$$B = \frac{4\pi^2}{Gm_s}. \tag{2.27}$$

The important quantity is not the constant B per se, but the way that it determines the product Gm_s of the gravitational constant and the mass of the sun. If we could determine by astronomical observations the radius R and the orbit time T of a planetary motion, then from (2.26) we could find this product Gm_s. By inversion of (2.26),

$$\frac{Gm_s}{4\pi^2} = \frac{R^3}{T^2},$$

and multiplication by $4\pi^2$, we have an explicit expression for Gm_s.

$$Gm_s = 4\pi^2 \left(\frac{R^3}{T^2}\right)_p. \tag{2.28}$$

This expression refers to the motion of a planet around the sun, and to remind us of this, the suffix p has been attached to the last group of quantities. But exactly the same kind of expression will be relevant to the motion of a satellite about the earth (say),

$$Gm_e = 4\pi^2 \left(\frac{R^3}{T^2}\right)_{\text{earth satellite}} \tag{2.29}$$

or indeed of a satellite about any other planet:

$$Gm_p = 4\pi^2 \left(\frac{R^3}{T^2}\right)_{\text{planetary satellite}} \tag{2.30}$$

Now the quantities on the right can be measured astronomically in ways that will be described shortly, so that those on the left can be calculated. Remember that we can still only calculate the *products* of the gravitational constant G and the various masses; we do not yet know what the individual quantities are. It is like knowing how much interest is to be paid on a loan, without knowing either the amount of the loan or the rate. If, in addition, we knew either of these we could calculate the other. Nevertheless, the ratios of the products above do give the ratios of the masses of the sun and the planets to that of the earth, say. As soon as we know *one* of these masses themselves (instead of just the products like Gm_s), we can calculate them all.

The measurement of the orbit time T presents no difficulty in principle; we merely observe a particular planet or satellite to see how long it takes to complete one circuit. It is perhaps a little less obvious to see how we can measure the radius R, whether it represents the radius of the earth's orbit about the sun or that of the moon about the earth. Nowadays, the best way to measure these distances is by the reflection of a pulse of radio waves from, say, the moon; the same technique that is used in radar. The distance of the moon is just half the time required for the pulse to complete its round trip times the velocity of light, which is known accurately from laboratory experiments. Previously, less direct methods had to be used.

One of the simplest and most ancient techniques involved a slight ramification of the triangulation methods that surveyors use. To measure the distance of the moon from the earth, a long, carefully measured base line is established on the earth, as shown in Figure 10, and from each end the angle between a chosen point on the moon and the base line is measured with great care. The length of the base line and the two angles fix the triangle, and with the aid of a little trigonometry the distance between the earth and the moon can be found simply. Although this method is simple in principle, it should be remembered that great accuracy is required, since very small differences in angle are involved in the direction of the moon at the two ends. For a base line of 1000 miles, the angles differ by only about 0.2 degrees! Nevertheless, the measurements have been made and it is found that, for the moon,

$$R_m = 240,000 \text{ miles}$$
$$= 3.84 \times 10^5 \text{ km.}$$

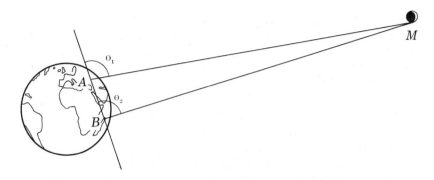

Figure 10. Measurement of the distance of the moon by triangulation. Observatories at *A* and *B* simultaneously measure the angles θ_1 and θ_2 between a point of the moon and the direct line between them. These angles, together with the length of the base line fix the triangle and enable the distance of the moon to be calculated.

The radius of the earth is about 4000 miles, so that the radius of the orbit of the moon is approximately 60 times the earth's radius.

In principle, the same method could be used for the sun, but since it is so much more distant, the angle differences are so much smaller that it is impossible to measure them with any accuracy at all. What is really needed is a very long base line, much longer, in fact, than the diameter of the earth. Although this may seem impossible, it can, in fact, be achieved.

Figure 11 shows how it is done. An observer on the earth waits until he sees that the moon is exactly half full—the moon's disc is divided between light and shadow precisely along a diameter. This means that the lines between him and the moon and between the moon and the sun are exactly at right angles. He then measures the angle Φ that *he* sees between the moon and the sun. Now, in Figure 11, *EMS* is a right-angled triangle, so that from the definition of the cosine, $\cos \Phi = ME/ES = R_m/R_e$ where R_e is the distance from the earth to the sun. If we now multiply both sides of the equation by R_e and divide by $\cos \Phi$, we have explicitly that $R_e = R_m/\cos \Phi$. The distance R_m is already known,

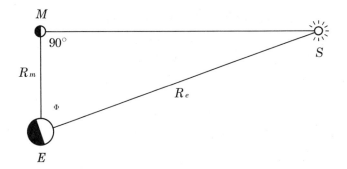

Figure 11. An ancient method for measuring the distance of the sun. When the moon's disc, as viewed from the earth, is exactly half illuminated by the sun, the angle EMS is 90°; if the angle Φ is measured and R_m known, the triangle is determined. The relative sizes of earth, moon and sun and their separations are of course distorted greatly for purposes of clarity.

and if he measures Φ, then R_e is found simply. In this way, it can be shown that

$$R_e = 93,000,000 \text{ miles}$$
$$= 150,000,000 \text{ km}$$
$$= 1.5 \times 10^8 \text{ km},$$

or 24,000 earth radii! The distance from the earth to the sun is 24,000 times the radius of the earth.

It is rather absurd to express these distances in centimeters, since the numbers involved are so huge. It will be convenient later to use these units, however, so that we might as well be consistent. There are 10^5 cm in each km, so that

$$R_m = 3.84 \times 10^{10} \text{ cm},$$
$$R_e = 1.5 \times 10^{13} \text{ cm}.$$

With these figures, we are now in a position to make use of our equations (2.28) and (2.29) to find, in particular, the ratio of the masses of the earth and the sun. For the orbit of the earth around the sun, T is the length of the terrestrial year:

$$T = 365\tfrac{1}{4} \text{ days,}$$
$$= 365\tfrac{1}{4} \times 24 \times 60 \times 60 \text{ seconds,}$$
$$= 3.16 \times 10^7 \text{ seconds, nearly.}$$

The radius R of the earth's orbit is given above, so that

$$Gm_s = \frac{4\pi^2 R^3}{T^2} = \frac{4 \times \pi^2 \times (1.5 \times 10^{13})^3}{(3.16 \times 10^7)^2} \text{ c.g.s. units}$$

$$= 13.2 \times 10^{25} \text{ c.g.s. units,}$$

a very large number.

Next, let us turn to equation (2.29), describing the motion of a satellite about the earth. The moon is the best known of these, and for it,

$$T = 27.3 \text{ days}$$
$$= 2.36 \times 10^6 \text{ seconds,}$$

and $\qquad\qquad R_m = 3.84 \times 10^{10}$ cm.

Therefore, from (2.29),

$$Gm_e = 4\pi^2 (R^3/T^2)_{\text{moon}}$$

$$= \frac{4\pi^2 (3.84 \times 10^{10})^3}{(2.36 \times 10^6)^2},$$

$$= 4.0 \times 10^{20} \text{ c.g.s. units.}$$

Remember that G is still unknown, so that the mass of the earth continues to elude us. We are in a position, however, to work out the *ratio* of the earth's mass to that of the sun, for

$$\frac{m_e}{m_s} = \frac{Gm_e}{Gm_s} = \frac{4.0 \times 10^{20}}{13.2 \times 10^{25}} = \frac{1}{330,000}.$$

Evidently, the earth, massive as it is, is only a speck of the sun.

It is interesting to notice incidentally that we could have calculated the product Gm_e in an entirely different way. In the last section, we found a relation (2.24) between this, the radius $\mathcal{R}$ of the earth and the gravitational acceleration g:

$$g = \frac{Gm_e}{\mathcal{R}^2},$$

so that

$$Gm_e = g\mathcal{R}^2.$$

Now, as measured by a pendulum, g is approximately 980 cm sec^{-2}, while $\mathcal{R} = 6400$ km $= 6.4 \times 10^3$ km $= 6.4 \times 10^8$ cm. Consequently, on substitution of these figures into the last formula, we have

$$Gm_e = 980 \times (6.4 \times 10^8)^2$$
$$= 4.0 \times 10^{20} \text{ c.g.s. units, precisely}$$
as found above.

These calculations are characteristic of the way in which the simple properties of the solar system are deduced from the laws of gravitation and mechanics. The mass ratios of the planets with natural satellites can be found in the same way that we found m_e/m_s. For example, Jupiter has a satellite (its fifth) with a twelve-hour period and a circular orbit with radius 115,600 miles, or 178,000 km. From this information, the interested reader can find the product of G and the mass m_j of Jupiter and thence the ratio m_j/m_e of the mass of Jupiter to the mass of the earth. (The answer comes out to be considerably greater than 1.)

Some planets, like Venus, appear to have no natural satellites and these methods cannot be used. It is possible, however, to infer the mass ratio of Venus by a more complicated procedure. The orbit of Venus is, of course, determined primarily by the gravitational attraction of the sun, but the attraction of the other planets as they sweep by introduces small disturbances or perturbations of its elliptical orbit. Perhaps fortunately, these are too small to have been noticed in Kepler's day. More recently, the study of planetary perturbations has become of great importance in the astronomy of the solar system. The planet Neptune was, indeed, discovered in the last century as a result of the anomalous motion of Uranus. It was discovered that the orbit of Uranus suffered perturbations that could not be accounted for on the basis of the attractions of the known planets, and Adams in England and Leverrier in France proposed independently that they were the result of a further planet, as yet undiscovered. Not only did they do this, but they calculated (on the basis of Newton's laws) just how large this planet should be and what orbit it should follow. When the observational astronomers looked, there was Neptune!

2.7 THE EQUATORIAL BULGE

The earth is, of course, very nearly spherical and rotates about its axis once every twenty-four hours. As a consequence of this rotation, a body at rest relative to the surface of the earth at the equator is not at rest relative to the center of the earth, but is experiencing a circular motion about this center with a radius equal to the radius of the earth and an 'orbit time' of twenty-four hours. According to the laws of mechanics, therefore, there must be a net unbalanced force on the body in order to provide the inwards acceleration associated with this circular motion. In alternative, but rather imprecise language, there must be an additional (fictitious) 'centrifugal force'; the weight of a body at the equator is the result of both the gravitational attraction to the earth and the 'centrifugal force' of its rotation about the center of the earth.

Figure 12 represents a mass m suspended on a string at the equator. There are two genuine forces acting on the mass. The first is the tension in the string acting upwards, which is what one would measure with a spring balance, and what we have called its weight mg. The second force is the gravitational attraction of the earth, mg_t, say, acting downwards, where g_t is the true acceleration due to gravity alone, that is, the acceleration that would be measured if there were no rotation of the earth. The *net* force acting downwards is the difference between these two, $mg_t - mg = m(g_t - g)$; this must be just the amount needed to provide the inwards acceleration of the circular motion, namely $v^2/\Re$, where v is the speed of a point on the equator relative to the center of the earth and $\Re$ is the earth's radius. Consequently, by the laws of motion, the *net* force = (mass) × (acceleration):

$$m(g_t - g) = mv^2/\Re,$$

or
$$g_t - g = v^2/\Re.$$

But the circumference of the earth is $2\pi\Re$ and the time taken to complete a circuit is $T = 24$ hours, so that the speed

$$v = \frac{2\pi\Re}{T},$$

and on substitution in the last equation, we have

$$g_t - g = \left(\frac{2\pi\Re}{T}\right)^2 \frac{1}{\Re} = \frac{4\pi^2\Re}{T^2}.$$

The difference $g - g_t$ between the apparent acceleration due to gravity (modified by the earth's rotation) and the acceleration

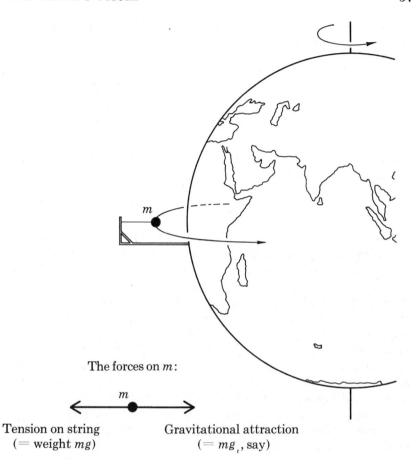

The forces on m:

Tension on string   Gravitational attraction
(= weight mg)   (= mg_t, say)

Figure 12. A body suspended 'at rest' at the equator is actually rotating with the earth about its axis once in twenty-four hours; it is in circular motion about the axis of the earth. The force required to keep the body in this circular path is just the small difference between the tension in the string supporting it (what we have called its weight) and the actual gravitational attraction toward the earth.

that there would be without rotation of the earth, is the negative of this last expression:

$$g - g_t = -\frac{4\pi^2 \mathfrak{R}}{T^2},$$

and the fractional difference,

$$\frac{\delta g}{g} = \frac{g - g_t}{g} = -\frac{4\pi^2 \mathfrak{R}}{gT^2}. \tag{2.31}$$

Since $\mathfrak{R} = 6.4 \times 10^8$ cm, $T = 24$ hours $= 8.6 \times 10^4$ seconds and $g = 980$ cm/sec² nearly, it follows by substitution that

$$\frac{\delta g}{g} = -3.46 \times 10^{-3}.$$

Now, a similar mass at either of the poles is just revolving about its own center once every twenty-four hours, and its center is not moving anywhere relative to the center of the earth. It is experiencing no acceleration, and consequently its weight is the result of the true gravitational attraction alone. *If* the earth were a perfect sphere, then g_t would be the same at both the equator and the poles, and the actual acceleration that we measure—that is g itself—would vary by the quantity that we have just calculated: it would be about 3.5 parts per thousand smaller at the equator than at the pole. Careful measurements show that there is a difference of this kind but that it is more like 5.3 parts per thousand. Apparently, this simple analysis is a part, but not the whole of the story. This first model of a completely spherical earth seems not entirely adequate.

In what respects could it be deficient? The assumption of spherical symmetry is one aspect that is immediately open to question. If the rotating earth were entirely liquid, it would bulge out a little at the equator: the gravitational force of cohesion would tend to keep the liquid gathered into a sphere, but the 'centrifugal force' associated with the rotation would tend to cause the liquid in equatorial regions to fly outwards, and the equilibrium would be maintained by the balance between the two. The assumption of a liquid earth is, even on the face of it, far from silly, since a good fraction of the earth's surface is covered by water. This bulge would have the effect that a body at sea level at the equator is a little *farther* from the center of the

earth than one at sea level at the poles, so that the true gravitational force on the equatorial body is a little *less*. This effect is
at least in the right direction to account for the discrepancy between our simple model and the observation, but it remains to be
seen whether this kind of revision can account in detail for the
magnitude of the difference.

In the more refined model, then, the earth is to be regarded as
a slightly flattened fluid sphere—an oblate spheroid. The degree
of flattening (or oblateness) is to be determined by this balance
between gravitational and 'centrifugal' forces, and once the
shape is determined, the surface distribution of the gravitational
acceleration is to be deduced. If $\mathcal{R}_e$ represents the equatorial radius of the earth and $\delta\mathcal{R}$ the difference between this and the
polar radius, then it turns out that the flattening, expressed as
$\delta\mathcal{R}/\mathcal{R}_e$, is not very different from $\delta g/g_t$:

$$\frac{\delta\mathcal{R}}{\mathcal{R}_e} = 0.0037 \simeq \frac{1}{297}.$$

In other words, the polar radius of the earth's spheroid is shorter
than the equatorial radius by one part in three hundred, nearly,
or about 21 km.

The only remaining step is to find the distribution of g on the
surface of the spheroid and to compare this with what is actually
observed on the earth. This time the agreement is found to be
very much better—the systematic variation of g between the
poles and the equator appears to be well described by this model:
we conclude that it has some elements of truth and that the earth
really does possess a polar flattening and an equatorial bulge.

These days, artificial satellites are used to determine the shape
of the earth to very much higher precision than was possible
before. Since the earth is distorted slightly from a spherical
shape, the gravitational field in its immediate neighborhood is
not exactly spherically symmetrical; by careful tracking of the
small perturbations of a satellite orbit, the asymmetry can be
found very accurately. It has been discovered that there are very
small departures even from the spheroidal shape; these presumably have something to do with the distribution of mass below
the surface of the earth. Local and rather irregular variations in
the gravitational acceleration are also measured in many neigh-

borhoods, and again one might guess that these are the result of local geological inclusions of different density from the surroundings.

After all this, where do we stand in our search to find the mass of the earth? We have managed to find the product Gm_e of this mass and the gravitational constant; we know the *product* but not each factor separately. We know the ratios of the planetary masses and that of the sun, but again, the *ratio* but not the numbers themselves. We have found many things, but despite our best efforts, we have not yet found what we really seek. In this last section, though, we did uncover something that is strange —if we assume that the earth is entirely liquid and not solid at all, then the shape that it would assume and the variation of the gravitational acceleration g at the surface is consistent with what is actually observed.

This fact provokes questions. Why *is* this 'liquid earth' model so successful? In other words, why is the solid earth so close to being the same shape that it would assume if it were liquid? The oceans are thousands of kilometers wide but only about four deep; the high mountains stand only about six kilometers above the ellipsoid. These are both much less than the equatorial bulge and are a tiny fraction of the earth's radius. Could it be that the 'solid' earth cannot support protuberances or hollows much bigger than this? Perhaps the 'solid' earth is not so firm after all.

3

The Mass of the Earth

3.1 CAVENDISH'S EXPERIMENT

Sometimes, science is like mountaineering: the summit may be clearly visible but the path to it is tortuous. We may climb many other mountains—achieving great satisfaction on the way —before our objective is attained. In our search for the mass of the earth, we have found many things, but our original goal remains ahead. We are close, though; we know the product of the gravitational constant and the mass of the earth, and if only we could measure G, we would be there.

The direct measurement of G would appear, in principle, to be simple. Since we have asserted that the gravitational attraction between two bodies is a universal property, the force being given by

$$F = G\frac{m_1 m_2}{r^2}, \tag{3.1}$$

then all that we have to do is to take two spheres in the laboratory with masses m_1 and m_2, with a distance r between their centers and to measure the force F of attraction between them. The equation can be rearranged in the form

$$G = \frac{Fr^2}{m_1 m_2},\tag{3.2}$$

and since all the quantities on the right can be measured directly, G can be found by simple calculation. But the existence of a force of gravitational attraction between bodies of manageable size is not a matter of ordinary experience at all; we *feel* no such force when we hold two bodies close. Evidently, on a scale like this, the forces are so tiny that they are below the threshold of our senses; if there is to be any hope of detecting and measuring them, it is necessary to devise an extraordinarily delicate balance.

The success of such an experiment must have seemed most improbable, since it sought to measure an effect whose existence had been inferred only from the motion of the heavenly bodies and whose relevance to laboratory objects was not at all suggested by ordinary experience. Nevertheless, the experiment was undertaken in 1798 in a room in London by Henry Cavendish, an eccentric grandson of one of the Dukes of Devonshire—the implausible experiment which worked.

It is evident that we need masses as great as can be managed conveniently in order that the force of gravitational attraction be as large as possible; yet, as Cavendish realized, they must be supported in such a way that an almost unimaginably tiny force between them can be measured. The solution that he found (and the one generally used in experiments of this kind today) is illustrated in Figure 13. Two identical masses, m_1, joined by a rigid light rod so that they form a kind of dumb-bell, are suspended by a long, thin ribbon attached to the center of the rod. Another two identical masses m_2 are brought near and then fixed; the force of attraction causes the masses m_1 to swing toward the fixed masses, being restrained only slightly by the twisting of the ribbon. The force is then measured in terms of the degree of twisting and of the elastic properties of the ribbon.

A supporting fiber in the shape of a ribbon seems to be the best that we could choose, since it can be made fairly wide in order to be strong enough to support the masses m_1 without breaking,

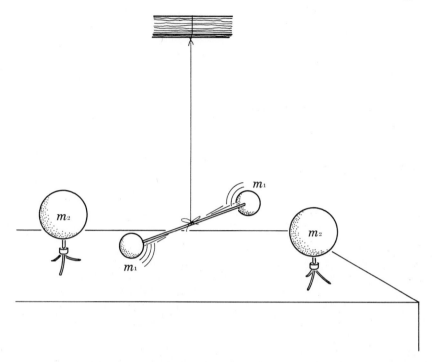

Figure 13. Cavendish's Experiment. The gravitational attraction between the fixed masses m_2 and the suspended masses m_1 is measured by the amount that the dumb-bell turns when the masses m_2 are placed in position.

and at the same time thin, so that it twists an appreciable amount under the influence of a very small torque. A torque is defined in mechanics as the product of a force times the perpendicular distance to the point about which it acts; the torque in Cavendish's experiment can be calculated simply in terms of the geometry and of the force that we seek to measure. Thus, in Figure 14, the gravitational force F acts on m_1 toward the center of m_2; if d represents the distance of the center of m_1 from the point of suspension of the dumb-bell, the perpendicular distance from this suspension point to the line of action of the force is the length of the line OP, or $d \cos \theta$. The torque result-

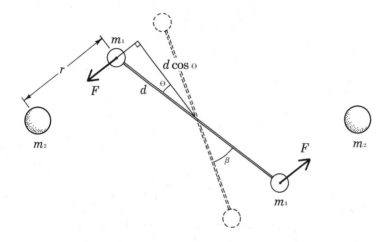

Figure 14. The geometry involved in Cavendish's experiment. The initial orientation of the dumb-bell is shown by the dotted outline. When the masses m_2 are placed in position the suspended masses swing through an angle β before equilibrium is restored.

ing from one pair of spheres is therefore $Fd \cos \theta$, and since there are two identical pairs, the total torque $\mathfrak{I}$ is $2Fd \cos \theta$. From Newton's law of gravitation, equation (3.1), therefore,

$$\mathfrak{I} = 2 \left(\frac{Gm_1m_2}{r^2} \right) d \cos \theta,$$

or

$$G = \frac{\mathfrak{I}r^2}{2m_1m_2d \cos \theta}. \tag{3.3}$$

Everything on the right of this equation can be measured readily with the exception of the torque $\mathfrak{I}$ that results from the gravitational attraction and is balanced exactly by the restoring torque produced by the twisting of the fiber. This can be found either by an auxiliary experiment or by calculation from the elastic properties of the material from which the fiber is made. The torque required to twist a fiber of length l through an angle β (Greek beta) is found from elasticity theory to be directly proportional to β and inversely proportional to l:

$$\Im = k\beta/l, \tag{3.4}$$

where the constant k depends on the shape of the cross-section and on the elastic nature of the fiber material. From this equation, it can be seen that any specific kind of fiber (with its characteristic k), twisted through a given angle β requires a torque $\Im$ that decreases as the length l increases. To observe *small* torques, as in Cavendish's experiment, we need a long length l of fiber. But to actually measure the constant k, to determine the degree to which the fiber twists under torque, we can perform a supplementary experiment on a sample of the same fiber that is very short—now, for a given angle β, the torque required is much larger and more easily measurable by direct methods. If we multiply both sides of equation (3.4) by l and divide by β, we have

$$k = \frac{\Im l}{\beta}.$$

In the supplementary experiment with the short fiber, all quantities on the right of this equation can be measured, so that k can be calculated. This number is characteristic of the kind of fiber itself, and so it can be used in equation (3.4) and applied to the twisting of the much longer fiber of the same kind in Cavendish's experiment.

The expression (3.4) for $\Im$ can be substituted into the previous equation (3.3) so that the gravitational constant

$$G = \frac{k\beta r^2}{2m_1 m_2 ld \cos \theta}, \tag{3.5}$$

where k is the fiber constant (already found in the auxiliary experiment), β is the angle of twist of the fiber of length l which supports the masses m_1 in the main experiment, r is the distance between the suspended masses m_1 and the fixed masses m_2, d is half the distance between the two suspended masses and θ is the angle shown by the geometry of Figure 14. All of these quantities can be measured directly, and from this the gravitational constant G itself is calculated.

This is the historic experiment which Cavendish performed to provide the missing piece of this part of the puzzle. In order to give some appreciation of the tiny forces involved, it might be

remarked that the gravitational attraction between two spherical masses, each of one kilogram, whose centers are separated by
10 centimeters is less than one-billionth of the weight* of either
sphere! Nevertheless, the experiment was successful in detecting
and measuring this force, and it must be regarded as one of the
tours de force of 18th century experimental science. It has been
repeated many times since with far greater accuracy, and modern determinations point to a value, in c.g.s. units,† of about

$$G = 6.67 \times 10^{-8} \text{ gm}^{-1} \text{ cm}^3 \text{ sec}^{-2}. \tag{3.6}$$

---

* Remember, weight is a force. cf., Section 2.2.
† These units are rather strange; it might have been simpler to call
them 'c.g.s. units' (Appendix 1) without specification of their exact
nature. They can, however, be found most simply from equation (3.2).

$$[F] = [\text{mass} \times \text{acceleration}],$$

$$= \left[\frac{\text{mass} \times \text{velocity}}{\text{time}}\right],$$

where the square brackets mean 'the units of.' Since, moreover,

$$[\text{Velocity}] = \left[\frac{\text{distance}}{\text{time}}\right],$$

$$[F] = \left[\frac{\text{mass} \times \text{distance}}{(\text{time})^2}\right].$$

In c.g.s. units then,

$$[F] = \frac{\text{gm cm}}{\text{sec}^2}.$$

In equation (3.2), r is a length (cm), while m_1 and m_2 are masses (gm),
so that

$$[G] = \left[\frac{Fr^2}{m_1 m_2}\right] = \frac{\text{gm cm}}{(\text{sec})^2} \frac{(\text{cm})^2}{(\text{gm})^2}$$

$$= \frac{(\text{cm})^3}{\text{gm} (\text{sec})^2}$$

$$= \text{gm}^{-1} \text{ cm}^3 \text{ sec}^{-2},$$

as given in equation (3.6).

It is interesting to realize that of all the 'fundamental physical constants' (some others being the speed of light *in vacuo,* Plank's constant h, the electron charge e) the one known to the lowest degree of accuracy is G. The experiment is a difficult one, even today, and this, in retrospect, makes Cavendish's accomplishment even more remarkable.

3.2 THE EARTH'S MASS

At last, we can find the mass of the earth. In Section 2.6, we calculated that

$$Gm_e = 4.0 \times 10^{20} \text{ c.g.s. units,}$$

whence, with the value given above for G,

$$m_e = \frac{4.0 \times 10^{20}}{6.67 \times 10^{-8}},$$

$$= 6.0 \times 10^{27} \text{ gm.} \tag{3.7}$$

This is another of these enormous numbers. Even expressed in tons (6.6×10^{21} tons mass), it is little better. Can we interpret this in terms of something more easily visualized?

3.3 THE FIRST REAL CLUE: DENSITY

The mass of the earth as well as its volume have finally been found. Both numbers in themselves are so huge that it is difficult to visualize them. But from them we can find the average density of the earth and this provides our first firm indication of its inner constitution.

In Section 2.1, it was shown that the earth's volume is about 1.1×10^{12} cubic kilometers. There are 100 cm in 1 m and 1000 m in each km, and so 10^5 cm per km. One cubic kilometer therefore contains $(10^5)^3 = 10^{15}$ cubic centimeters (c.c. or cm³), so that in c.g.s. units, the volume of the earth

$$V = 1.1 \times 10^{27} \text{ c.c.}$$

The average density $\bar{\rho}$ (Greek rho) is the mass per unit volume:

$$\bar{\rho} = \frac{m_e}{V} = \frac{6.0 \times 10^{27}}{1.1 \times 10^{27}},$$

$$= 5.5 \text{ gm/cc (or gm cm}^{-3}). \tag{3.8}$$

The density of ordinary water at $0°$ C is, to a sufficient accuracy for our present purposes, just 1.0 gm cm^{-3} (the c.g.s. system of units was set up so that this would be so), and accordingly, the average density of the earth is just 5.5 times the density of water; its relative density is 5.5.

Now this, at last, is a very interesting number. The density of rocks commonly found near the surface of the earth is easily measured by geologists—it varies from 2 to 3.5 times the density of water. The *average* density of these surface rocks is only about 2.8 relative to water. The interior of the earth is certainly under great pressure; under the influence of this the density of rocks may be a little greater, but certainly not enough to account for the difference between 2.8 and 5.5. It would appear that whatever the center of the earth is made of, it must have a density *much greater* than that of ordinary rock in order to bring up the average to the value 5.5 that we have found.

Immediately then, we are faced with another question: what could it be, this dense material at the center of the earth? The most familiar heavy materials are the heavy metals, iron, nickel, lead, chromium and so on. It seems sensible to expect that whatever the core of the earth is made of, it must be something fairly common, just because there is so much of it inside the earth. The commonest of the heavy metals by far is iron. Near the surface it is almost always oxidized, but this need not be so at great depth, where, as we shall see, it is certainly hot. The relative density of the metal in ordinary circumstances is about 8 and under great compression rather more, so that a core of iron could easily bring the average density up to 5.5. Other metals, like lead, gold and mercury have higher densities but they are comparatively rare. One would not expect to find a huge block of gold at the center of the earth since on the surface it is found only very occasionally as tiny specks or, at the most, small nuggets. Iron, then, seems a not unlikely provisional guess—probably mixed with other less common heavy metals like nickel, for few things are found in the natural state to be pure.

So let us make the tentative hypothesis that the core of the earth is made mostly of iron and perhaps some other lesser ingredients. This fits the few facts that we know at this stage and seems a sensible choice. Remember, however, that it is still tentative, and should we discover facts with which this model cannot be reconciled, it will have to be discarded. Later in this book, however, further evidences will be found that point in the same direction and the greater the accumulation of these, the greater the credence that we can accord this model.

Having found the average density of the earth, we are confronted with new questions. The density of the earth is evidently not uniform, since the surface rocks are so much less dense than the average. How is the density distributed in depth? Is the earth like a huge chocolate coated candy, with light rocks on the outside and a uniform core (of iron, perhaps) inside? Or does the density increase gradually from the surface as the depth increases? Or is the truth somewhere in between; with a series of layers as in Figure 15 with the density becoming greater as the layer depth increases? Is the interior solid or liquid? These questions point the direction in which we must now go.

3.4 PRECESSION

As it follows its orbit about the sun, the earth spins on its axis, once every twenty-four hours. The direction of the earth's axis is not perpendicular to the plane of the orbit, but is tilted by $23\frac{1}{2}°$; the seasons of the year are a result of this. But long ago, astronomers noticed that the direction in space of the axis of the earth's rotation is not quite constant, but is changing very gradually as the years go by. The angle between the normal to the orbit plane and the axis remains at $23\frac{1}{2}°$ but the axis itself is revolving about the perpendicular, once in 26,000 years! The same effect can be seen in the motion of a spinning top. The top is spinning rapidly about its axis, but if this is not quite vertical, the axis itself rotates lazily as shown in Figure 17. As the spin of the top decreases, the rotation of the axis becomes more agitated until finally the top falls over. This effect, the slow rotation

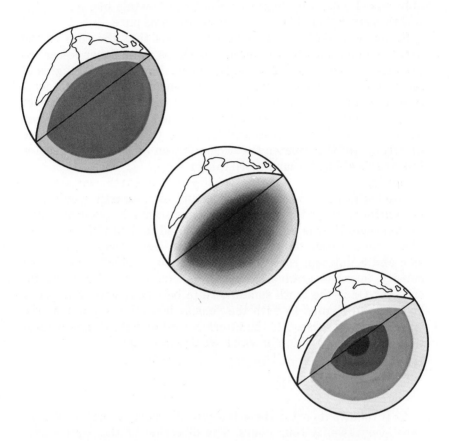

Figure 15. With a knowledge of only the average density of the earth, it is possible to imagine many ways
in which the actual density may vary with depth. For
example, the earth may consist of a uniform layer of
light rocks overlying a uniform, denser interior as
shown at the top. Alternatively, the density may increase steadily toward the center as illustrated in the
second sketch. Again, the earth may consist of a series
of layers, each slightly denser than the one above, as
shown at the bottom. These models may all give the
same average density; we need further information to
discriminate among them. It will, in fact, turn out
that none of these is very close to the truth.

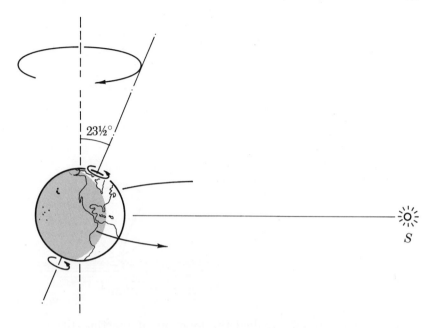

Figure 16. The precession of the earth's axis. The earth is spinning about its own axis, once in twenty-four hours. But the axis of the earth itself is tilted by 23½° and this axis rotates about the vertical (the perpendicular to the plane of the orbit) once in 26,000 years, as a result of the slight equatorial bulge and resulting imbalance.

of the axis, is called precession, and the precession of the earth's axis will be found to provide some further insight into the nature of its interior.

The existence of this phenomenon is a consequence of Newton's laws of motion which, of course, govern the dynamical behavior of spinning bodies. To understand something of its nature, we must consider briefly the way in which the distribution of mass in a body influences its dynamical properties in spin. Now, in the original form of Newton's laws, it was shown that the mass of a body is the measure of its inertia—its resistance to acceleration when a force acts upon it. The analogous quantity

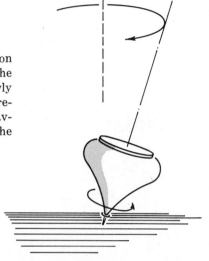

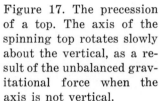

Figure 17. The precession of a top. The axis of the spinning top rotates slowly about the vertical, as a result of the unbalanced gravitational force when the axis is not vertical.

in rotational motion is called the moment of inertia—the measure of its resistance to acceleration of spin (angular acceleration) when a torque is applied.* The moment of inertia of a body depends, not only on its mass, but on its shape and size, and on the way in which the mass is distributed. The more the mass is concentrated toward the axis of rotation, the smaller is the moment of inertia, and conversely, the further it is spread away from the axis, the greater the moment of inertia.

Unless the body happens to have spherical symmetry, the moment of inertia also depends on the axis about which the rotation takes place. A garden rake can be spun from rest over and over about an axis along the center of the handle as in Figure 18(a) with only a small torque; to achieve the same rotation rate in the same time but end on end about an axis perpendicular to the center of the handle, as in Figure 18(b), requires a much larger torque. This is so because in the latter case, the mass is distributed at much greater distances from the axis of rotation, and the moment of inertia about this axis is correspondingly more.

---

* Torque is defined in Section 3.1.

Again, a closed umbrella standing on its point can be turned as in Figure 19 by applying only a small torque to the handle. But if the umbrella is opened, a much greater torque is required to produce the same spin. The total mass is the same, but by the opening of the umbrella, much of the mass is redistributed further from the axis, and the moment of inertia is correspondingly increased.

For a *uniform* solid sphere of mass m and radius $\mathcal{R}$, the moment of inertia about an axis through the center can be shown to be given by

$$I = \tfrac{2}{5}m\mathcal{R}^2; \tag{3.9}$$

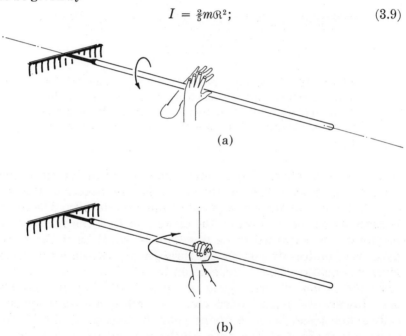

(a)

(b)

Figure 18. The moment of inertia of a garden rake about an axis along the handle (a) is relatively small, so that it can be spun about this axis with a small torque. About an axis perpendicular to the handle, however, (b), the moment of inertia is much greater since the mass is distributed further from the axis. It requires a much larger torque to produce the same rate of turning in the same time.

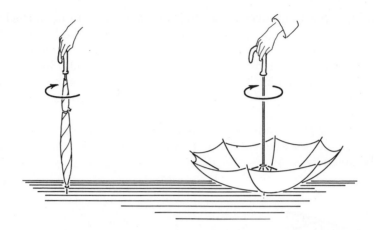

Figure 19. When an umbrella is opened, part of its mass is redistributed further from an axis along the stem, and its moment of inertia increases. It requires a greater torque to produce the same spin in a given time.

because of the spherical symmetry, the moment of inertia is the same about an axis through the center in *any* direction. But we already know that the earth is *not* of uniform density. The mass is concentrated more toward the center, so that the moment of inertia can be expected to be *less* than it would be if the same mass were uniformly distributed throughout; less than the value given by equation (3.9). The amount by which it is less will give some indication of the degree of concentration of the earth's mass toward its center. Moreover, the earth is not quite spherically symmetrical because of the polar flattening, so that *if* we could spin it about an axis through the equator, we would expect to find a slightly different moment of inertia than the one appropriate to spin about the axis through the poles.

We cannot, of course, set the earth into rotation about an axis through the equator, but fortunately the natural motion of the earth can be used to find the moment of inertia that would be appropriate if we could. This is where the precession of the earth's axis is involved. The rotation of the earth is not a pure spin about the polar axis; this axis itself is rotating about a line perpendicular to the plane of the orbit about the sun (Figure 16). The complete rotation of the earth is the composite of these two; the polar rotation part involves in its dynamics only the moment of inertia about the polar axis, but the precessional part involves more—since the axis of the precessional motion is between the polar and equatorial directions, both the polar and the equatorial moments of inertia are involved.

Now the dynamics of precession are rather difficult, but the very existence of the phenomenon depends critically upon the imbalance between the polar and equatorial moments of inertia— a perfectly symmetrical sphere does not precess at all. We can therefore use the observed rate of precession to calculate this imbalance. Moreover, the fractional difference between these two (the difference divided by the polar moment of inertia) can be found quite independently from the knowledge of the degree of flattening in the shape of the earth that we acquired from the gravity measurements. When these two distinct lines of investigation are put together, it is possible to calculate the actual moments of inertia of the earth. It is found that, about a polar axis, the earth's moment of inertia

$$I_e = 0.3337 m \Re^2, \tag{3.10}$$

instead of $0.4\ m\Re^2$ for a perfectly uniform sphere.

As we had guessed, the moment of inertia of the earth is less than it would be if its density were completely uniform. This indicates that the mass is concentrated toward the center, but does not allow us yet to find the detailed distribution of density with depth. It applies a constraint to the distribution; it is useful in eliminating many distributions that might be imagined without giving a single, unambiguous answer for the actual distribution. Nevertheless, on the basis of the results already established, we can begin the construction of provisional models for the density distribution inside the earth; models which will almost certainly have to be revised as evidence accumulates.

3.5 CONJECTURES AND CONSTRAINTS

In the preceding pages, several important properties of the earth have been found: its radius, the degree of polar flattening, its average density and its moment of inertia about a polar axis. In addition, the average density of the surface rocks is known to be about 2.8, though we cannot be at all sure how important this is. It *may* be no more relevant to the density of the interior than is the color of the skin of an apple to the color of its inside. Nevertheless, let us inquire to what extent these overall properties enable us to infer something about the density distribution and to what extent the matter is still open. Let us *conjecture* that the density is distributed in one or two simple ways and see what constraints these overall properties impose. There is one additional requirement dictated by common sense—the density can hardly decrease anywhere as the depth increases. If it did, the denser material would overlie the less dense and if the deep interior is at all fluid, it would tend to overturn—the denser region would literally sink through the less dense and we would end up once more with the less dense on top. Note also that it is adequate in these models to assume spherical symmetry, since the polar flattening is such a small fraction of the earth's radius.

In the first model, let us suppose that, as illustrated in Figure 20, the earth is like a great chocolate coated candy—with the density ρ_1 uniform between the surface, of radius $\mathfrak{R}$, to an inner sphere of radius $\mathfrak{R}'$, where it jumps to a larger value ρ_2, inside which it is again uniform. Assume that $\rho_1 = 2.8$, the average value of the relative density of the surface rock; neither ρ_2 nor $\mathfrak{R}'$ is known, but will have to be calculated on the basis of the constraints that we have established, namely, that the overall average density is 5.5 and that the moment of inertia coefficient is 0.3337. There are two constraints; these are sufficient to determine the two unknowns ρ_2 and $\mathfrak{R}'$.

The analysis of this model is entered in detail in Appendix 2.2. The calculations there lead unambiguously to the results,

$$\mathfrak{R}' = 0.82\mathfrak{R},$$
$$\rho_2 = 7.7. \tag{3.11}$$

The distribution of density represented by this solution is shown in Figure 21. The discontinuity that we have imagined (the boundary between the core and the surface region) must lie at

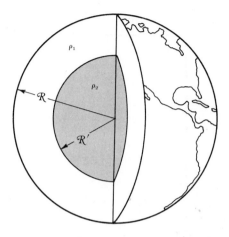

Figure 20. A simple model of the interior of the earth in which the known average density and the known moment of inertia are used to provide constraints. In this two-layer model, the density of the interior region and its radius are to be found. It still contains many arbitrary aspects, however, and is subject to modification as observational evidence accumulates.

0.82 times the earth's outer radius. The density inside this region must be 7.7—surprisingly close in fact to the density of iron at normal temperature and pressure. This is suggestive, but not too much significance should be attached to it at this stage. The inner core appears to be surprisingly large but this is a quirk of the geometry—about half the whole volume of the sphere lies between 0.82 times the radius and the outer surface.

This model is interesting in that it shows how the quantitative properties of the density distribution can be found on the basis of the constraints and a simple conjecture about the nature of the density variation. To gain some idea about how sensitive the answers are to the particular conjecture made, let us construct an alternative model and analyze it in the same way. Suppose, this time, that there are no discontinuities but that the internal density increases uniformly in proportion to the depth below the surface as shown in Figure 22. Again, there are two unknowns

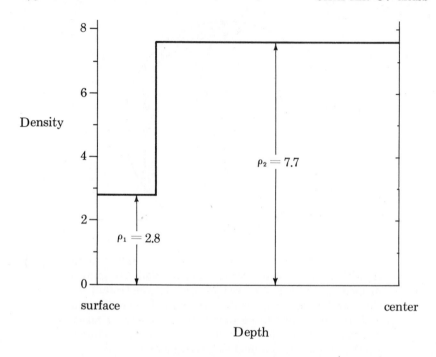

Depth

Figure 21. Results from the analysis of the two-layer model. The distribution of density with depth is shown; the discontinuity (the surface between the inner and outer regions) being found at 0.82 times the outer radius.

in this model, the density ρ_s of the rocks just below the surface* and that ρ_c of the material at the center. Again, there are two constraints, the known average density and the known moment of inertia coefficient. The calculation this time involves some integral calculus and will not be given at all, but the answers turn out to be

---

* We already know that the average density of rocks at the surface is about 2.8, but in view of our present uncertainty about how relevant this is to the density (say) five miles below, we prefer to regard ρ_s as unknown.

$$\rho_s = 2.8,$$
$$\rho_c = 12.5.$$
(3.12)

According to this model, the density of the rocks just below the surface is exactly the same as the average density found independently by direct measurement. The equality of these two cannot be regarded as more than coincidence; we would have been

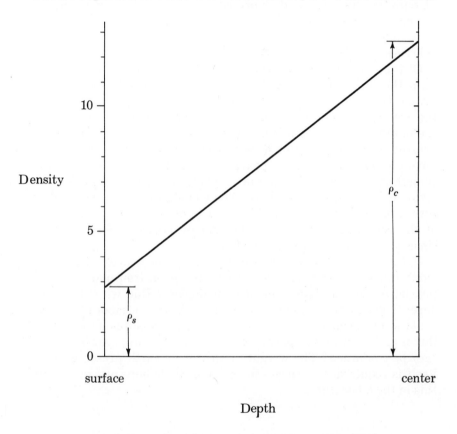

Figure 22. The distribution of density with depth postulated in our second simple (and very arbitrary) model. The densities at the surface and the center are regarded as unknown and are to be calculated from the average density and moment of inertia figures already established.

gratified if they had turned out to be even approximately the same. The density at the center of the earth is larger than was given by the previous model, nearly twice as large but not twenty times. Neither model should be taken too seriously—each will be found later to be gravely deficient—but the degree of consistency between them leads one to anticipate that whatever the actual distribution of density, it is probably not more than perhaps 15 at the center of the earth and probably not less than about 7. It would require a very extreme model to get answers much outside these limits.

Of the two, the second model is probably a little more realistic than the first. The planet is compressed internally by its own gravitation—the center being under great pressure because of the weight of all the material above. Whatever the nature of the material in the core, it is certain therefore to be highly compressed, to have a greater density than the same material would have on the surface. It appears important, therefore, to know something of the magnitude of the internal pressure in the interior of models such as these. The calculation is of course different for each model considered, but in either case, the pressure at the center is found to be enormously large—several million times the pressure of the atmosphere.

If these are at all representative of the pressures inside the earth itself, it is not hard to believe that even iron may be compressed to almost twice its normal density. But we cannot be sure. It would be tremendously helpful if, in the laboratory, we could study properties of materials under pressures as large as these, and at high temperatures; but in what apparatus would they be contained? The weight of the whole earth pressing upon itself is required in nature—there seems little hope of ever doing this in the laboratory.

3.6 THE DENSITIES OF OTHER PLANETS

What of the other planets? How similar to the earth or how different are they in their internal constitution? The first firm indication we had about the nature of the interior of the earth came from its average density—can we in a similar way find the average densities of the other planets?

Kepler's laws and Cavendish's experiment provided the keys that we needed to find the mass of the earth, and they will unlock other doors as well. Let us, for example, consider Mars, with its two satellites Phobos and Deimos. The first of these has an orbit of radius 9000 km and takes 7 hours 39 minutes (27,500 sec) to revolve around Mars; the second is distant 23,000 km with an orbit time of 30 hours 21 minutes (1.08×10^5 sec).

The form (2.30) of Kepler's third law, namely,

$$Gm_p = 4\pi^2 \left(\frac{R^3}{T^2}\right)_{\text{planetary satellite}}$$

enables us to calculate very simply the mass (m_p) of the planet about which these satellites revolve. With the figures for Phobos,

$$\left(\frac{R^3}{T^2}\right)_{\text{Phobos}} = \frac{(9 \times 10^8)^3}{(2.75 \times 10^4)^2} = 1.05 \times 10^{18} \text{ c.g.s. units,}$$

while for Deimos,

$$\left(\frac{R^3}{T^2}\right)_{\text{Deimos}} = \frac{(2.3 \times 10^9)^3}{(1.08 \times 10^5)^2} = 1.05 \times 10^{18} \text{ c.g.s. units.}$$

The fact that these numbers are the same is no coincidence; it is a further verification of Kepler's third law and confirms that the law of gravitation governs the motion of these satellites about Mars as it does the orbits of the major planets about the sun. The substitution of this ratio (for either satellite) into the previous equation leads to

$$Gm_p = 4\pi^2 \times 1.05 \times 10^{18} = 4.15 \times 10^{19} \text{ c.g.s. units.}$$

But from Cavendish's experiment, the gravitational constant G is 6.67×10^{-8} c.g.s. units, so that the mass of Mars,

$$m_p = \frac{4.15 \times 10^{19}}{6.67 \times 10^{-8}} = 6.3 \times 10^{26} \text{ c.g.s. units}$$

(or grams). This is about a tenth the mass of the earth, but the radius $\mathcal{R}_m$ of Mars is also rather less, only 3400 km, or 3.4×10^8 cm. Consequently, the average density of Mars, the mass divided by the volume:

$$\text{Average density} = \frac{m_p}{(\frac{4}{3})\pi \mathcal{R}_m{}^3},$$

$$= \frac{6.3 \times 10^{26}}{(\frac{4}{3})\pi(3.4 \times 10^8)^3},$$

$$= 3.95,$$

only about twenty per cent less than the average density of the earth. When we remember that Mars is smaller than the earth, so that the compression of the material at the center is less, we might with some basis conjecture that the internal constitution of the planet is not very different from that of our own.

These calculations are typical of the way in which the densities of the other planets with natural satellites can be found. The results are summarized in Table I. The inner planets, Mercury, Venus, Earth and Mars all have similar densities but the larger outer planets are something of a surprise. Their densities are very much lower (Saturn being, on average, less dense than water in spite of its huge size and mass) and this alone indicates that

TABLE I.

Planet	Radius (km)	Mass Relative to the Earth	Average Density
Mercury	2,420	0.054	5.4
Venus	6,100	0.815	5.1
Earth	6,400	1.000	5.5
Mars	3,380	0.108	3.95
Jupiter	71,350	317.8	1.33
Saturn	60,400	95.2	0.68
Uranus	23,800	14.5	1.60
Neptune	22,200	17.2	2.25
Pluto	3,000	0.8 ?	?

their constitutions must be very different from that of the earth. Being farther from the sun, their temperatures are very much lower than those found on the earth and many materials ordinarily gaseous here may be liquid or solid there. Spectroscopic studies indicate that their atmospheres consist largely of hydrogen, but who knows what their internal structures are like?

Some of the satellites of Saturn are even less dense than is the parent planet. The nearest (Mimas) has a density only 0.3 times that of water, less than almost any solid material on earth! Is Mimas possibly a loose collection of dust or a kind of porous celestial sponge? We can only conjecture.

4

Earthquakes and Seismic Waves

4.1 EARTHQUAKES

In our search to discover the heart of the earth, we have gone about as far as we can with only the resources of mechanics applied to the earth as a whole. To progress further, we need some kind of probe to search deep into the earth. Such a probe is offered, perhaps surprisingly, by earthquakes.

Earthquakes and volcanoes are the most evident manifestations of ponderous activity below the surface of the earth. It is natural that we think of them as closely associated, but as a general rule there is often little *direct* connection between the two. In many places, such as in Los Angeles, California, earthquakes are not uncommon but there are no active volcanoes in the vicinity. Nevertheless, the parts of the earth's surface most prone to earthquakes are also those where volcanoes are sometimes found. When a volcano does erupt, there are usually earth tremors and these are very useful, as we will see later, in developing an understanding of some of the properties of volcanoes. Earthquakes

are, however, very much more common than are volcanic eruptions, though fortunately few are severe enough to upset the
equilibrium of buildings and of their occupants.

Most earth tremors are so small that they are not even noticed
without sensitive instruments. Some tremors are initiated by
superficial causes, such as heavy traffic on a road or the beating
of surf on a beach. The disturbances produced in this way, called
microseisms,* *can* travel a great distance; it has been shown that
tremors of this kind in Colorado are sometimes produced by the
incidence and reflection of great ocean storm waves at the coast
of California, about 1000 miles away. Nevertheless, microseisms
are surface effects which, by their very nature, cannot tell us
much about the deep interior. Other small earth tremors do appear to originate at great depths, and these will be the object of
our further attention. An earthquake of slight to moderate intensity will be noticed by a person standing still as a trembling
or a swaying of the earth underneath his feet—a person walking
may notice nothing. In a fairly strong earthquake, hanging
lamps may sway and chairs slide about the room. Only in an
intense earthquake do buildings collapse, chasms appear and
rocks tumble from mountains—these are rare but widely reported and well remembered.

In 1950 there was a very intense earthquake between Assam
in India and Tibet. The area is high, mountainous and sparsely
inhabited, so that there was very little human damage. But the
whole face of the country was changed; mountains collapsed,
sliding into valleys, blocking rivers, creating new lakes and
filling old ones. In 1935, there was a much *less* intense earthquake at Quetta, now in West Pakistan, a crowded garrison town
in the days of the old Indian Empire. The center of the earthquake was close to the town. In a few moments, the town was
destroyed and 30,000 people killed. When earthquakes do strike
cities, the greatest damage is frequently the result of secondary
effects, such as fire or flooding. A severe earthquake struck the
Tokyo area in 1923 at a time when the midday meal was being
prepared; braziers overturned, setting fire to many of the lightly

---

* Greek, *seismos* = earthquake.

built Japanese houses. An appalling fire spread rapidly; although few were killed by the earthquake directly, almost 150,000 people died in the subsequent fires in Tokyo and a further 100,000 in Yokohama.

Earthquakes are much more frequent in some regions than in others, and the way that the earthquake zones are distributed is most interesting—it is a piece of observational evidence to which we will have occasion to return. The map in Figure 23

Figure 23. The earthquake zones of the earth.

shows the regions where earthquakes occur most frequently. They appear to lie in three distinct zones. One circles the Pacific Ocean almost completely—New Zealand, Japan, the Aleutians, California and Chile are all noted for their earthquakes. From this, a branch extends along the Himalayas and the Mediterranean Sea to Spain. The third zone stretches right down the middle of the Atlantic Ocean. The *fact* that these are the regions of greatest activity is established by observation and patient recording; the *reason* why these particular regions should be favored above others will emerge only gradually as the different pieces of the puzzle fit together.

Particularly on the shores of the Pacific Ocean, an earthquake will frequently cause movements of the sea bed, which result in wave surges that can travel from one side of the ocean to the other. These are popularly called tidal waves (but erroneously so, since they have nothing at all to do with the tides); more accurately they can be called by their Japanese name, *tsunamis.*

In the deep ocean, a tsunami may consist of a series of waves, a group, in which the wavelength or distance between successive crests may be miles, and the wave height only a few feet at most. Indeed, ships can sail through the tsunami while the crew remains unaware of the fact. As the sea bed rises toward the land to a depth of only a few hundred feet, however, the wave height (shown in Figure 24) increases as it does when surf forms on a beach. The whole scale is now much larger though; in a tsunami the sea level often recedes before the arrival of the

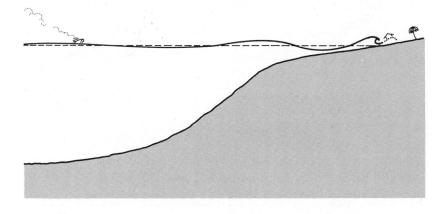

Figure 24. A tsunami in deep water (at the left) is barely perceptible. When it reaches shallow water, the height of its crests and the depth of its troughs increase greatly and it may cause severe damage. The broken horizontal line represents the undisturbed ocean surface level.

first crest, which then may rise twenty feet above the normal water level, crashing over the beach, through trees and houses for half a mile.

What causes earthquakes? A first guess, guided by the observations already described, would be that they are the result of stresses, gradually accumulated and suddenly released by a local fracture, a breaking of the rocks deep in the earth. The very existence of earthquakes implies that the earth is not a static thing, but is constantly moving, settling and adjusting. Nor is the face of the earth unchanging; it responds to the slowly evolving balance of forces beneath. There are hints of many kinds to be gleaned from these things, but a more immediate question must be answered first. How can earthquakes cast light on the nature of the earth, not only in their immediate vicinity but elsewhere, to the very core of the earth itself?

4.2 THE SEISMOGRAPH

A stone, thrown into a tranquil pool, disturbs the surface violently; from the point of impact a train of waves spreads out in ever widening circles, gradually dying out as they move toward the distant shore. When a bomb explodes, the sudden expansion of the burning gases causes a shock wave to travel outwards rapidly, weakening as it spreads. Near the explosion, the shock wave can cause great damage; at greater distances it can only rattle windows and be heard as a dull thud. In the same way, an earthquake, which we presume to be a violent local disturbance of some kind, produces a train of waves moving outwards possibly to the ends of the earth.

If we are to make use of seismic or earthquake waves in our exploration of the interior of the earth, we must first be able to detect them even when they are so weak as to be imperceptible to our unaided senses. Having done this, we must then exercise our wit and patience in an endeavor to unravel the messages that they contain, to interpret what we measure in such a way that it will illuminate, even darkly, the internal structure of the earth.

There are two kinds of information that we will seek. The first concerns the occurrences themselves; they are distributed geographically as shown in Figure 23, but how are they distributed in depth? To answer this question, we must devise a way to locate the depth of the disturbance centers from observations at the surface. When we have done this, further questions will present themselves—*why* do earthquakes apparently occur more frequently at some depths than others? What properties of the material in the earth are associated with earthquake fractures and how can we infer from their distribution according to depth, something of the way in which the material itself changes with depth? These questions will be provoked by a knowledge of the locations of earthquake centers; different information will be derived from the passage of the waves from their source through the earth to distant places. As the waves move outwards from their source, their speed depends on the nature of the material through which they move, their scattering and reflections depend on the structures that they encounter on their way. By a careful examination of the form of the waves as they arrive back at the surface, we will seek to discover something not only about their place of origin, but also about where they have been.

Before we can do these things, however, we need an instrument that can detect the arrival of seismic waves and measure their properties. Such a device is called a seismograph. Modern seismographs are complex and delicate instruments but the important idea underlying their operation is simple.

The problem is to measure the shaking of the earth beneath us, even when it is so tiny that it is to our senses imperceptible. If anything is rigidly attached to the earth, it shakes too, moving with the underlying earth and having no relative motion. If, however, a large mass is balanced on very 'soft' springs, as in Figure 25, then as the ground shakes, the great inertia of the mass will inhibit motion—as the earth moves beneath it, the springs will be extended a little, but being 'soft,' will result in only a small unbalanced force. The mass is large and the force is small, so that by Newton's laws the acceleration is small; the mass stands almost stationary in spite of the earth movement. It is very similar to a heavy, well-sprung car traveling over a rough road. The wheels shake up and down as they pass over

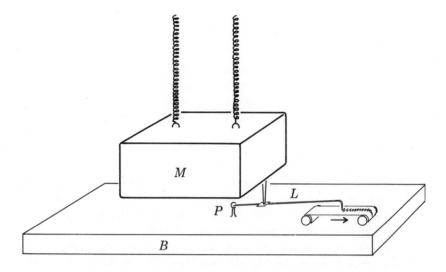

Figure 25. A simple seismograph. The heavy mass M is suspended from soft springs while the base B is rigidly attached to the earth. When the earth shakes, the pivot P moves while the mass M hangs steadily. This causes the lever L to shake and the motion is recorded on the moving chart.

the bumps, but, as a result of the 'soft' springs, the car body hardly moves at all vertically.

A seismograph, then, is in essence a heavy mass suspended from springs so that the earth can oscillate beneath it without causing appreciable motion of the mass. A device is needed to record the relative motion of the mass and the earth; since the motion is generally so small, there has to be a reasonable amount of amplification in the recording device so that the result is readily discernible.

An instrument like this should be placed in a quiet location, preferably underground, far from the local disturbances produced by traffic and heavy construction. It will record the arrival of seismic waves, but an understanding of how it responds involves the nature of the waves themselves and to this we will now turn.

4.3 SEISMIC WAVES

Seismic waves are less familiar than many other kinds of wave motion. Water waves or the waves on a stretched rope are easily visualized and in many respects they exemplify some of the basic qualities associated with wave motion in general; there is much in common between these on the one hand and, on the other, the sound waves in the air which we hear but cannot see and the seismic waves in the earth which we may not be able to sense at all without a seismograph. From these more familiar examples, let us extract the essential qualities of what we call a 'wave,' in terms of which we can describe the way that an earthquake disturbance moves through the earth.

A water wave consists of a series of alternate crests and troughs which move across the surface. The distance between successive crests (or successive troughs) is called the wavelength (Figure 26): the speed at which a crest moves is called the wave speed. An important property of waves is that the water itself is *not* moving with the wave speed. A smooth train of water waves passes beneath a bubble on the surface of the pond. The bubble, carried by the water under it, moves up and down, to and fro, but is not carried along with the wave crest.*
In the waves on a stretched cord, it is only the wave motion, the curved *configuration* that moves along the length of the rope; the cord itself moves from side to side. The wave propagates through the medium, whether it is the water or the rope. The wave speed is therefore frequently called the propagation speed to distinguish it from the speed of the shaking motion of the medium itself. In the same way, a sound wave passes through the air, a seismic wave through the earth while the particles themselves shake to and fro. A wave is, in essence, a pattern; as the medium shakes the pattern propagates.

Let us probe a little deeper. Why are there such things as

---

* Unless the waves are foaming at the crest, but this is an extreme condition particular to water waves and not characteristic of other types of wave motion.

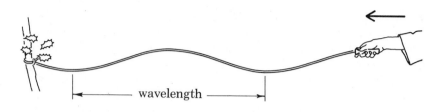

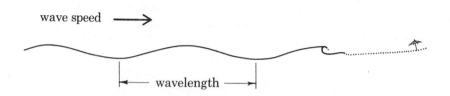

Figure 26. Rope waves and water waves. The wavelength is the distance between successive crests or
troughs. The wave pattern propagates along the rope
from right to left while the rope itself shakes up and
down. The water wave pattern travels to the right
while the individual water particles move to and fro.

waves at all? Despite their obvious differences, what is common
to a water surface and a stretched cord that allows this pattern
that we call a wave to pass over the surface and along the cord?
There are, it seems, two attributes, both of which are very
simple but both essential. The first is *connection;* the fact that
movements in one part are influenced by those in neighboring
parts. The cord is continuous, so that if one part moves, the
nearby parts must move in sympathy. If we shake the end of the
cord, the section near our hand but not touching it is pulled into
motion also. If we disturb the water surface with a paddle, the
movement is not confined to the water particles actually touching
the paddle, but extends some distance away as the water swirls
around. The second attribute common to these two is the existence of a *restoring force* when the configuration is altered from
its rest position. The tension in the cord tends to hold it straight;

when a section is pulled sideways in any direction, there is a force, resulting from the tension, that resists the deformation and seeks always to restore the original rest configuration. If we depress a part of the water surface, there is a force, acting upwards, that resists the deformation, that seeks to restore the water surface to its original horizontal level. If we raise an isolated hummock, the weight of the water in the hummock (the force) acts downwards, again resisting the change and working to restore the undisturbed state.

Both of these, the connection and the existence of a restoring force brought about by a disturbance, are essential. If either is absent, there can be no propagation of a wave pattern. For example, in Figure 27, a row of pendulums is suspended from a

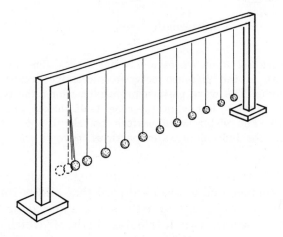

Figure 27. In a row of pendulums hanging from a rigid bar, each has a restoring force which will cause it to swing individually. The series of pendulums, however, lacks connection so that a wave pattern cannot propagate along the row.

rigid bar. If any pendulum is displaced, say to the right, there is certainly a restoring force tending to return it to its equilibrium position. If it is let go, it accelerates to the left, swings, and overshoots the vertical. On the other side, the force now opposes the motion; the bob slows down and finally stops at the other end of its swing, whereupon the process is repeated as the bob swings back. Each pendulum has a *restoring force,* it can swing individually, but the motion of each is irrelevant to the next in line. The assembly as a whole lacks *connection* and no wave pattern can propagate along the line. If, initially, they are all stationary, and we set the end pendulum in motion, the others remain at rest. Again, in Figure 28, the smoke from a

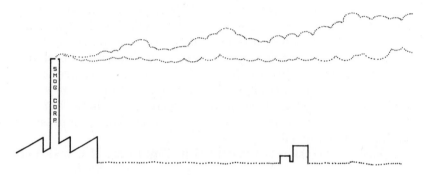

Figure 28. The billows in a smoke plume have connection but lack a restoring force. They are carried by the wind but do not propagate through the air as a wave does.

stack is carried by the wind. Just as in the water motion around the paddle, the neighboring particles of air influence one another's motion; they certainly possess connection. However, in this case there is no restoring force. If part of the smoke plume billows upwards, there is no force to restrain it; it just continues to do so. In this example, the second essential attribute is absent and again no wave pattern can propagate along the plume. To be sure, the plume may be irregular, but the irregularities are carried *with* the wind, they do not propagate *through* it.

A wave, then, is a pattern that propagates *through* a medium while the particles in the medium shake to and fro. For a wave to exist, it is necessary to have both connection between neighboring parts of the medium and a restoring force to resist deformation. These statements are abstractions drawn from familiar examples—how can we apply the abstractions to the less familiar seismic waves in the earth? The rocks and other materials in the interior certainly possess connection; to understand how seismic waves propagate we have only to consider the modes of deformation and the associated restoring forces in the earth.

Iron and rocks, like most materials, are elastic to some extent; they become deformed if loads are applied to them and, unless the load is too great, recover when it is removed. The statement can be rephrased in the following way. When solid materials are deformed, the deformation brings into play a restoring force that seeks to return the material to its original size and shape. There are many possible kinds of deformation but two are basic: a pure compression, a change in volume without change in shape and what is called a pure shear, a change in shape but not volume. When both volume and shape change, both compression and shear are involved.

A pure compression is illustrated in Figure 29. If a pressure,

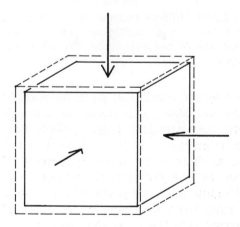

Figure 29. A pure compression involves change in volume but not shape. When a cube, whose initial outline is shown by the broken lines, is subjected to uniform pressure in all directions, it remains a cube but its volume is decreased.

uniform in all directions, is applied to a specimen, it is compressed in all directions and its volume is reduced. Its shape, however, is not altered; a cube of the material remains a cube though the length of each side (and hence its volume) diminishes a little. In the compressed state, the restoring force that resists the deformation opposes and balances the applied pressure that causes it. The magnitude of this restoring force depends on the material (some are more easily compressed than others) and on the extent of the compression, the reduction in volume per unit volume that the specimen has suffered. For any particular material, the pressure producing the compression (and so the balancing pressure p resisting it) is *proportional* to this fractional change in volume. Symbolically:

$$p \propto \frac{\text{Reduction in volume}}{\text{Original volume}}.$$

Different materials have different constants of proportionality, so that if we write

$$p = e_c \frac{\text{Reduction in volume}}{\text{Original volume}}, \tag{4.1}$$

the constant e_c is a characteristic of the material. It is called the compression or bulk modulus; it has been measured in experiments with many materials and the results are tabulated in handbooks. The greater the bulk modulus, the greater the pressure required to produce a given fractional reduction in volume; the greater the resistance to compression. Note that in equation (4.1), the reduction in volume per unit volume is a fraction (one-tenth or one-hundredth as the case may be), so that if the equation is to be dimensionally consistent (if it is to make sense) the units on each side must be the same and so the bulk modulus e_c must have the same units as pressure. In iron, for example, the bulk modulus is about twenty million *pounds per square inch*.

A pure shear is shown in Figure 30. A cube is deformed into the shape called a parallelepiped; its shape changes but not its volume. To produce this deformation, we have to push tangentially on opposite pairs of faces and again, the force that is invoked by the deformation and that seeks to restore the original shape is proportional to the extent of the deformation. As be-

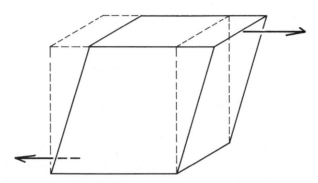

Figure 30. A deformation in shear involves change in shape but not volume. When forces are applied as shown to a cube, pushing along pairs of opposite faces, it is deformed into a parallelepiped. (Only one such pair is shown in the figure; unless the block is to topple forward, another is needed on the slant faces to balance the torque of the first.)

fore, different materials resist this kind of deformation more strongly than others, so that we can specify in a similar way a modulus of shear e_s that expresses the capacity for resistance to this deformation and again is a characteristic of the particular material concerned. A material with a high modulus of shear is relatively rigid while one with a low modulus is easily deformable. Again, e_s is measured in the same units as pressure.

There is something that should be noted at this point. It seems almost an aside, but later it will suddenly become of crucial importance. It is that liquids have the capacity to resist compression—their bulk modulus is appreciable—but they cannot resist shear. When deformed in shear they just flow; they offer no restoring force to a displacement of this kind and their shear modulus is zero.

It seems, then, that the response to deformation in solid materials is a little more complicated than the response to a disturbance of a water surface or a stretched string. The restoring forces depend on the kind of deformation, whether it is compression involving e_c or shear, involving e_s, or a combination of the two in which both may enter.

Now what kinds of simple wave pattern can we imagine to propagate through the interior of a solid? One possible type is shown in Figure 31, which illustrates the successive deformations of a part of the interior of the solid as the wave passes by. There is no distortion of the vertical planes (such as, for example, the end face) but they are displaced laterally relative to one another. At successive instants, the *pattern* moves to the right as the planes shake up and down; the motion of all the particles in any plane is at right angles or *transverse* to the direction in which the pattern (the wave) propagates. If we mark a tiny square in the material (the black one in the figure) and follow its deformation, we see that it is distorted from its initial shape to a rhombus, back to a square, overshooting to a rhombus of the opposite sense and back. The deformations of this tiny marked region are exactly those we have described as pure shear (Figure 30); the restoring forces caused by the deformation must involve only the shear modulus e_s. For this reason, waves of this kind are commonly called shear waves. When shear waves pass through the earth, they can be called alternatively 'S waves' (a useful mnemonic being 'shake waves'), and for reasons that will appear shortly, 'secondary waves.'

If we are to make use of the passage of these waves through the earth, we must know how the speed of propagation of the pattern is determined by the nature of the material through which it moves. This can be discovered by the same technique of dimensional analysis that we used in Section 2.3 to find the oscillation time of a pendulum. The first step is to write down all the quantities that we think might be relevant. In this instance, we know that the shear modulus e_s is going to be important since the deformation in the material involves simple shear and the shear modulus specifies the *restoring forces* involved in the motion. In addition, we would guess that the density of the material might be involved, since this relates to the *inertia* of the material shaking to and fro. Also possibly the wavelength of the pattern—since this is concerned with the *scale,* the size of the wave motion and we could hardly assert at the outset that patterns of all wavelengths propagate at the same speed. But this seems to be all; these three quantities should be sufficient to determine the wave speed. We would guess

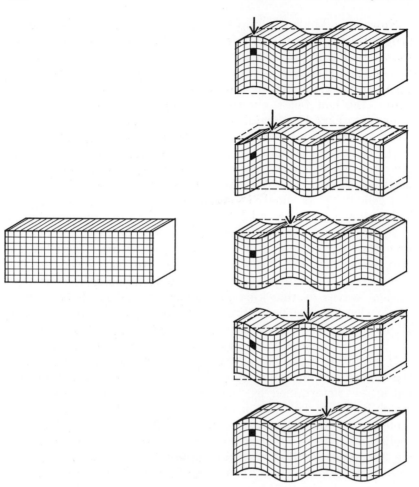

Figure 31. Successive stages of the deformation of a block of material by a shear wave. The undeformed block is shown on the left and the sequence progresses from top to bottom. A wave crest (marked by the arrow) passes through the block as the vertical planes in the material shake up and down. In the lowest configuration, the cycle is completed and each crest has moved on by one wavelength. The deformation of any particular marked area on the face involves alternating simple shear (Figure 30).

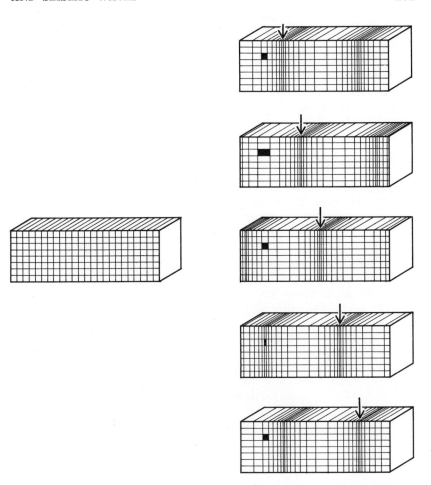

Figure 32. Successive stages in the deformation of a block of material by a compression wave. Again, the sequence progresses from top to bottom and a 'crest' of the pattern (the region of maximum compression, say) is marked by the arrow. This passes through the block as any small piece of material like the marked square shakes back and forth, suffering alternate compressions and expansions. Both the volume and the shape of this small marked region alternate as the wave pattern goes by.

that other properties should not be involved. For example, the bulk modulus should be irrelevant since the wave cycle does not involve any alternating compressions of the material. Also, the temperature or the chemical constitution should influence the motion only insofar as it affects the shear modulus or the density. Since we can think of no other relevant properties, we can assert that the propagation speed c_s of shear waves depends only on the shear modulus e_s, the density ρ (Greek rho) and the wavelength L, or symbolically,

$$c_s = \text{some function of } (e_s, \rho, L). \tag{4.2}$$

Now, we have to find the units in which the various quantities are measured. Being a speed,

$$[c_s] = \text{cm sec}^{-1},$$

where again, the square brackets mean 'the units of.' The shear modulus is, as was pointed out above, measured in the same units as pressure, or force per unit area. Force is, by its definition, mass times acceleration, so that

$$
\begin{aligned}
[e_s] &= [\text{pressure}] \\
&= \left[\frac{\text{force}}{\text{area}}\right] \\
&= \left[\frac{\text{mass} \times \text{acceleration}}{\text{area}}\right] \\
&= \frac{(\text{gm}) \times (\text{cm sec}^{-2})}{(\text{cm}^2)} \\
&= \text{gm cm}^{-1} \text{ sec}^{-2}.
\end{aligned}
$$

Next, density

$$
[\rho] = \left[\frac{\text{mass}}{\text{volume}}\right] = \frac{\text{gm}}{\text{cm}^3}
$$
$$
= \text{gm cm}^{-3},
$$

and the wavelength L is just a length:

$$[L] = \text{cm}.$$

The final task is to arrange a combination of e_s, ρ and L to give the same units as c_s. This last quantity does not contain 'gm,' which can be eliminated by taking the ratio

$$\left[\frac{e_s}{\rho} \right] = \frac{\text{gm cm}^{-1} \text{ sec}^{-2}}{\text{gm cm}^{-3}}$$

$$= \text{cm}^2 \text{ sec}^{-2},$$

which, as it happens, is the same as the units of (speed)^2. Hence, on taking the square root, we see that the only dimensionally consistent form of (4.2) is

$$c_s \propto \left(\frac{e_s}{\rho} \right)^{1/2}, \tag{4.3}$$

where again $\propto$ means 'is proportional to.' Evidently, the wavelength L is, after all, not involved—there is no way in which it can be incorporated to give a dimensionally correct statement, one which equates quantities measured in the same units.*

Just as in the pendulum problem, dimensional analysis can give no information about the constant of proportionality involved in (4.3). It provides the *form* of the relation but not the numerical constant. A more detailed calculation, which will not be given here, would show that the constant of proportionality is simply unity, so that in fact

$$c_s = \left(\frac{e_s}{\rho} \right)^{1/2}. \tag{4.4}$$

This result contains important information about the propagation of these S waves. The speed c_s does not depend on the wavelength, so that whatever wavelengths are generated by an earthquake, they will arrive *simultaneously* at a distant point. Also, such waves can pass only through a solid—a liquid, we recall, has no resistance to an elastic displacement in shear so that e_s is zero. If we substitute this into (4.4), it follows that c_s is zero for liquids—the wave does not propagate at all.

It should now be becoming clear how the properties of these waves can be used to provide information on the nature of the interior of the earth. By timing the passage between two points which are a known distance apart, the wave speed c_s can be

---

* This is, of course, reminiscent of the way that we found the mass of a pendulum bob to be irrelevant to the time taken for it to complete a swing. In dimensional analysis, it does not matter if we include in our list *more* properties than are actually involved, but we must be careful not to leave any out.

found—this gives directly the value of e_s/ρ for the material through which the wave has passed, even if it is deep inside the earth and inaccessible to direct measurement. It does not give the density ρ and elastic modulus e_s separately, but only their ratio; this is a limitation, however, that we shall have to accept.

The shear wave is not the only kind of wave pattern that we can imagine. Another is illustrated in Figure 32, which again represents a slab of the material at successive instants during the passage of the wave pattern. Here, however, the pattern consists of alternating compression and extension of the material between adjacent vertical planes; as the wave pattern moves to the right the vertical planes of the material are pushed backwards and forwards along the line in which the wave pattern moves. Waves with this general property are called longitudinal waves in contrast to transverse waves (for example, S waves) in which the material shakes in a lateral direction. If we follow the sequence of distortions of a particular square marked on the face of the slab (such as the black one in Figure 32), it can be seen to deform from a square to an extended rectangle, back to a square and then to a compressed rectangle as the wave pattern goes by. These deformations clearly involve changes in the volume of any tiny piece like this of the material so that the restoring forces invoked will depend on the compression modulus. But they also involve changes in *shape;* this as we pointed out is concerned with shear deformations, and as a result, the restoring forces will depend also on the shear modulus. Waves of this second type are called compression waves and their speed c_p is given in terms of the elastic properties of the medium by

$$c_p = \left\{ \frac{e_c + (\frac{4}{3})e_s}{\rho} \right\}^{1/2}, \tag{4.5}$$

depending, as we had anticipated, on both moduli e_c and e_s.

Since $e_c + (4/3)e_s = e_s + (e_c + 1/3\, e_s)$ is necessarily larger than e_s alone, it follows by comparison of (4.4) with (4.5) that c_p is larger than c_s; compression waves always travel *faster* than shear waves.* If there is a sudden disturbance at some point in

---

* In the surface rocks of the earth, c_p is some 5000 m/sec, while c_s is about 3000 m/sec.

the earth, producing both kinds of waves, then at a distant observatory the compression waves will arrive first and the shear waves later. For this reason, compression waves are often called primary waves; less formally, P waves, or 'push waves,' in contrast to the secondary, S, 'shake' or shear waves.

The expression (4.5) shows that compression waves, unlike shear waves, *are* able to pass through liquids and gases, even though the shear modulus e_s vanishes. In this instance, (4.5) reduces to

$$c_p = \left(\frac{e_c}{\rho}\right)^{1/2}, \tag{4.6}$$

which is not zero. Compression waves in air or water are simply sound waves, familiar to us all.*

4.4 LOCATING EARTHQUAKE CENTERS

When two cars, starting from the same place, travel steadily at different speeds in the same direction along a road, the distance between them constantly increases. A person, standing by the road will see one car pass and then the other, and the further he is from the starting point, the longer will be the time interval between the two. Precisely the same effect occurs with the P and S waves generated simultaneously at an earthquake center and traveling outward with different speeds. An observatory close to the earthquake will notice the arrival of the P wave front as shown in Figure 33 followed a very short time later by the S wave. The more distant the observatory, the greater the time interval.

The situation is illustrated most simply by a distance-time

---

* There is, in fact, another class of wave motions that can exist in the earth. These are surface, or interfacial waves which travel not through the interior of the earth but along its surface or along an interface that separates two layers of the earth's crust. They are rather like ocean waves—the motion is largest at the surface but decreases rapidly with increasing depth until far from the surface, it becomes imperceptible. Since they cannot penetrate to the heart of the earth, however, they will be of little interest to us in this exploration.

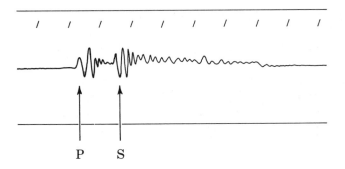

Figure 33. A seismograph record typically shows the separate arrival of the P and S wave fronts from a distant earthquake.

diagram such as Figure 34, in which the vertical axis represents distance from some point (taken here as the earthquake center) and the horizontal axis the elapsed time. Let us neglect for the moment the curvature of the earth's surface and suppose that

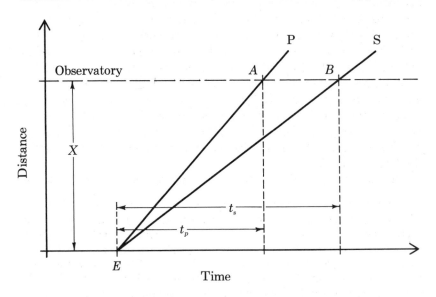

Figure 34. A distance-time diagram to find the distance between observatory and earthquake.

at some instant, represented by E, an earthquake occurs, sending out both P and S waves in all directions. The wave fronts move outwards; at any time t after the earthquake the P wave has moved a distance $c_p t$. This distance is clearly proportional to the elapsed time t; if it is plotted in the vertical direction, the course of the P wave front is indicated by a straight line sloping upwards from E. Similarly, the S wave front, moving with velocity c_s is represented by another line through E, but since, in a given time interval, it does not progress as far, the slope of the S wave line is *less* than that of the P wave line.

Now, suppose there is an observatory at a distance X from the earthquake center. *Its* location is represented by a horizontal line, at all times a distance X above E. The arrival of the P and S waves at the observatory is represented by the intersections A and B respectively, and the interval AB represents the time interval between the arrival of the two wave fronts at the observatory. *This* is what is measured; the slopes of the two lines (proportional to the speeds of the two types of waves) are known; the problem is to find X (since the location of the earthquake is unknown) and the time interval t_p, say, between the actual occurrence of the earthquake and the arrival of the P wave.

It is fairly obvious from the geometry that if the interval AB and the slopes of the two lines through these points are known, then the point of their intersection (E) can be found by a simple construction. The algebra is equally simple. If t_p represents the travel time and c_p the speed of the P wave, then

$$X = c_p t_p.$$

Also, if t_s is the travel time and c_s the speed of the S wave, this distance is also given by

$$X = c_s t_s.$$

Now, only the difference $t_s - t_p$ is known—the time interval between the two arrivals—together with c_p and c_s, of course. But from these equations,

$$t_s = \frac{X}{c_s}; \qquad t_p = \frac{X}{c_p},$$

and

$$t_s - t_p = X \left(\frac{1}{c_s} - \frac{1}{c_p} \right) = \frac{X(c_p - c_s)}{c_p c_s}.$$

Consequently, the distance between earthquake and observer is

$$X = \frac{c_p c_s}{(c_p - c_s)} (t_s - t_p); \qquad (4.7)$$

all the factors on the right hand side are either known or measured, so that X can be found. Finally, the time between the occurrence of the earthquake and the arrival of the first wave at the observatory is

$$t_p = \frac{X}{c_p},$$

and on substitution for X from equation (4.7),

$$t_p = \frac{c_s}{c_p - c_s} (t_s - t_p). \qquad (4.8)$$

So from simple observations at a single location, we can tell how far from us the earthquake was and exactly when it occurred. Nothing however can be said about the direction from which the waves came—this requires simultaneous recordings from two or more observatories. The geometry of this is straightforward. Imagine first that there is an earthquake very close to the surface of the earth (or perhaps a large explosion), whose location we wish to find, and that the arrival of the P and S waves is noted by observers at two different locations. Each can calculate, in the way that we have just described, the distance between his own observatory and the disturbance; on a map he can draw, as in Figure 35, a circle centered upon his observatory with its radius representing this distance. The other man does the same, and the intersection of the two circles is the location of the disturbance source. In general, of course, two circles intersect at two different points (if it is found that they do not intersect at all, then someone has made a mistake!); to decide which of these two points is the actual location, a third observatory is useful. This will provide another circle passing through one of the previous intersections, and this will clinch the matter.

The same procedure will work even when the earthquake center is not at the surface but at some depth. Three different observatories will provide measurements of the distance to the disturbance focus in the interior; we can think of these as the

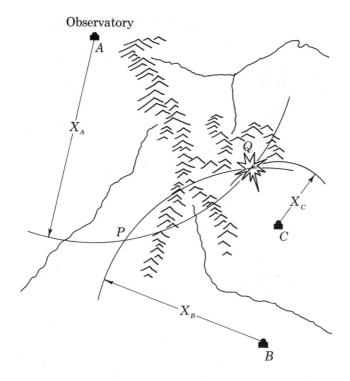

Figure 35. From a single observatory A the distance X_A to an earthquake center can be found simply from the construction of Figure 34, but not its direction. It might be anywhere along the circle of radius X_A. A second observatory at B measures in a similar way the distance X_B; with this information we conclude that the earthquake could have been at either intersection point P or Q. A third observatory, C gives X_C and fixes the earthquake unambiguously at Q.

lengths of three rods whose ends are fixed at the three observation points on the earth's surface. Only one tripod can be constructed with these rods all meeting at one point; this point fixes the center of the earthquake.

This is all very well if the speeds c_p and c_s of the wave propagation are known, but of course, for the central regions of the earth they are not. Indeed, their determination is the whole object of this study. There is no difficulty in measuring the wave speeds c_p and c_s for the rocks near the earth's surface, either by careful laboratory experiments on geological specimens or by direct measurement of travel times between a surface explosion and nearby points. The task of discovering how the wave speeds change as the depth increases involves patient observation and careful interpretation, but once again, the underlying idea is not complicated.

Imagine that the waves from an earthquake are recorded by a chain of observatories at different distances from the source, as shown in Figure 36. The waves that arrive at the nearest ob-

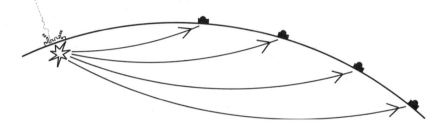

Figure 36. A chain of observatories at increasing distances from an earthquake center receives seismic waves that have penetrated successively deeper into the earth.

servatory have come by a shallow but direct path; they will have traveled at the speed appropriate to the surface structure of the earth. The waves arriving at a rather more distant observatory, even if they travel in a straight line, will have followed a deeper path; over at least part of their travel they will have sampled the material at a greater depth. Now if the propagation speed is variable, the distance traveled in time t is

$$X = \bar{c}_p t,$$

for the P waves, where $\bar{c}_p$ is the *average* propagation speed in the material that the wave has encountered along its path. Now, it is found that the average propagation speed *increases* as the distance between earthquake and observer increases, or as the maximum depth of the path increases. This means that a deeper traveling wave encounters material in which c_p is greater than it is at the surface. The waves traveling to ever more distant observatories have penetrated deeper into the earth, and if the disturbance is recorded on the other side of the world, the waves have traveled right through the center. This much is clear, but the actual problem of calculating from the observed wave speed, averaged over the paths, to the wave speed at a point a given distance below the surface, is far from trivial. The difficulties are, however, mathematical and not conceptual, so that they need not be described in detail. It is sufficient to gain some idea of the results, which are shown in Figures 37 and 38. There are many interesting aspects of these findings to which we will return.

One, however, might be noted now. The propagation speeds generally *increase* with depth. This means that a front of the wave pattern, moving to the right as in Figure 39, is traveling faster at a greater depth. The front will then move as shown, becoming tilted, and the direction of propagation (perpendicular to the wave front) turns upwards. As a consequence, the wave paths in the interior of the earth are not straight lines, but generally curve upward toward the surface as, indeed, was suggested by Figure 36.

Our ability to locate the centers of earthquakes, particularly their depth, provides information of the greatest importance. From observations of many earthquakes, it is found that most of them are centered at depths less than about 60 km (or 40 miles) ; below this the frequency of occurrence gradually decreases as the depth increases to some 300 km. Even beneath this, earthquake centers are sometimes found; they are far less common but their distribution seems to be about uniform between 300 and 700 km, below which it ceases altogether. If, as we have surmised, earthquakes are the result of a sudden local fracture, a release of accumulated stress, then it follows that considerable rigidity is required of the material before an earthquake *can* be generated. It is difficult to fracture honey. The fact that earthquake centers are sometimes found to depths as great as 700 km indicates that the material at these depths must still be rigid enough to support a gradually accumulated stress without flowing, until finally the stress concentration becomes

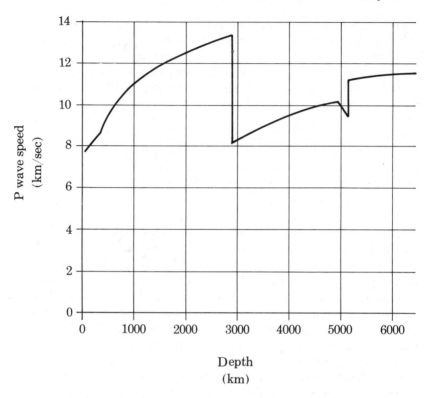

Figure 37. Measured distribution of P wave speeds
with depth (after Bullen). The speed generally increases with increasing depth except for the sudden
decrease at a depth of 2900 km and the weaker break
near the center.

so great that it breaks. Nevertheless, shallow earthquakes *are*
more common: is it that the stress accumulations develop more
frequently at depths less than 60 km, or is the material near
the surface more brittle?

4.5 THE MOHO

In 1909 there was a shallow earthquake in Croatia, now part
of Yugoslavia. Later, in Zagreb, a seismologist named Mohoro-

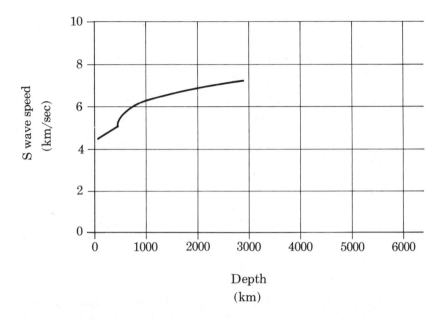

Figure 38. Measured distributions of S wave speeds
with depth (after Bullen). Below a depth of 2900 km,
S waves disappear.

vičić who was studying the records of this earthquake noticed something curious. At a certain distance from the focus,
the P and S waves arrived as they should, but a short time later
a second pair appeared! Yet there was no doubt that there had
been only a single shock. It was rather like an echo, but what
in the earth would produce an echo of these waves?

Echoes are most familiar when sound is reflected from a steep
rock cliff, or the blank wall of a building. However a surface
need not be hard to produce an echo—underwater sound re-
flects from the surface of the ocean very well, giving underwater
echoes that can confuse sonar operators. The important thing
is that the sound should encounter a sudden change in the nature
of the material and in the speed of propagation from one side to
the other—whether from air to rock or from water to air.
Mohorovičić realized that the apparent echo could be explained

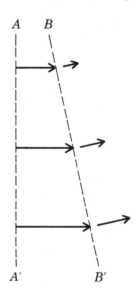

Figure 39. If the wave speed increases with depth, the wave paths tend to curve upwards. At one instant the wave front is at AA', and a little later at BB'. If the propagation speed at the depth A' is greater than it is at the depth A, then the distance $A'B'$ traveled in the interval is greater than AB. The front at BB' is then tilted and the waves, advancing perpendicular to the front, tend to curve upwards.

by a sudden change in the nature of the rock some distance down in the earth, by a discontinuity of some kind as in Figure 40. The travel time for the reflected waves was found by the interval between the second pair of P and S arrivals; with a knowledge of the speeds in the upper rocks, he calculated that this discontinuity, or change in structure, was at a depth of about 60 km, in Yugoslavia at least.* The discontinuity that he discovered now bears his name, but for fairly obvious reasons, it is frequently called the Moho.

The region below the Moho is called the mantle of the earth; that between the Moho and the surface, the crust. The crust is not uniform, as one might guess from the geological variations that are evident on the surface. In many places, multiple reflections occur, suggesting that the crust has subsidiary layers of different materials, particularly at relatively shallow depths. The Moho is called a 'discontinuity,' but there appears to be no reason to imagine it as a dividing sheet or surface, like that dividing the earth and the air or the ocean bed and the ocean

---

* This is very much less than the depth of the discontinuity that we imagined in our first tentative model of Section 3.5.

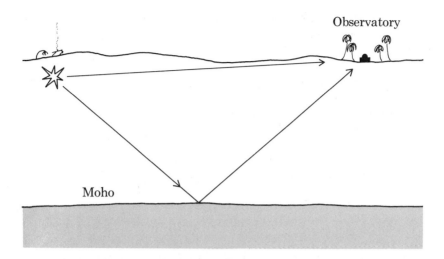

Figure 40. An earthquake near the surface can result in an echo of the seismic wave from a deeper discontinuity. Waves traveling along the direct path arrive at the observatory first, followed some time later by those that have been reflected at the discontinuity.

itself. It is certainly a relatively rapid change—in order to be able to reflect seismic waves, it must be no thicker than a wavelength or so. A more gradual change does not reflect waves well —sound, with wavelengths of a few centimeters, does not reflect well from a hillside covered in long grass. The seismic waves reflected from the Moho have wavelengths of perhaps 1 km, so the most we can say is that the Moho is a change from one material to another that takes place over at most 1 km. It *may* be an abrupt change, it may be more gradual. One way of settling this point would be to drill a hole through the crust to the Moho, and there were, indeed, plans for such a venture (the Mohole). The project was abandoned but one day it may be revived.

Below the Moho, in the upper regions of the mantle, it appears that the speed of P waves, c_p, is approximately 7 or 8 km/sec, while the speed of shear waves, c_s, is approximately 4.5 km/sec. This much can be measured directly by seismic observation; can these results be interpreted in such a way as to bear on the old problem—the density of the interior? Remember that the wave speeds are given by

$$c_s = \left(\frac{e_s}{\rho}\right)^{1/2}, \qquad c_p = \left(\frac{e_c + \frac{4}{3}e_s}{\rho}\right)^{1/2}. \qquad (4.9)$$

If we square both sides of the first of these,

$$c_s{}^2 = \frac{e_s}{\rho},$$

multiply by ρ and divide by $c_s{}^2$, we have

$$\rho = e_s/c_s{}^2.$$

Similarly, from the second of (4.9), $\rho = (e_c + \frac{4}{3}\ e_s)/c_p{}^2$. If we knew either e_p or e_s for the material below the Moho, we could calculate the density there. The problem is, of course, that we do not yet know what the material is; the best we can do is to make some likely guesses based on our knowledge of the geology of surface rocks to see whether their elastic properties and density are consistent with the wave speeds found. Matching in this way, geologists have been led to believe that the relative density of the material below the Moho is probably not very different from 3.3, compared with the average density of about 2.8 for the surface rocks above.

The depth of the Moho has been measured at many places on the earth. It varies, being generally less under the continents than the 60 km Mohorovičić found under Yugoslavia—30 or 40 km seems more characteristic. The thickness of the crust under the oceans is surprisingly and consistently very much less (Figure 41), typically only 5 km!

This is very curious and interesting. Why should the crust be six or eight times thicker under the continental land masses than under the oceans? It is true that the upper surface of the continents is higher than the ocean bed but not by 30 km; the oceans are only about 4 km deep and the average height of the continents above sea level is less than 1 km (3000 ft.). The crust beneath the continents is not only thicker, it extends *deeper* than it does under the oceans. It is almost as if the continents are floating like icebergs on the mantle, their submerged

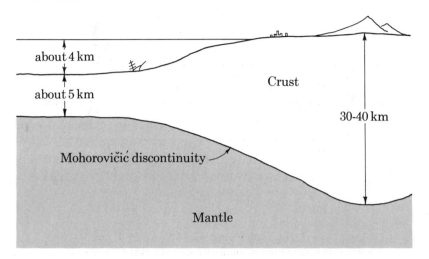

about 4 km

about 5 km

Crust

30-40 km

Mohorovičić discontinuity

Mantle

Figure 41. Seismic observations indicate that the continental crust is characteristically much thicker (30 to
40 km) than the oceanic crust (about 5 km); the Moho
is consistently much deeper below the continents than
below the oceans.

depths being a good deal greater than their heights. As far as
the densities are concerned, they *could* float; remember that the
density of the crust is about 2.8 while that of the mantle material is rather more—probably 3.3.

This view of 'floating' continents does not rest on these seismic
findings alone. It is supported by gravity measurements—careful determination of the true acceleration due to gravity g_t at
widely separated points on the surface of the earth. The continental rocks are considerably denser than water, so that at
sea level in a continental region, one might guess (Figure 42)
that the immediately underlying region should contain much
more mass than at another point at sea level in mid-ocean, with
4 km of water below. The law of gravitation, then, indicates
that the force of gravity should be rather larger on the continent, but experiments show that in general, *it is not*. It is very
nearly the same, whether measured on land or on a ship at sea.
This is another curious finding, but is consistent with the seismic

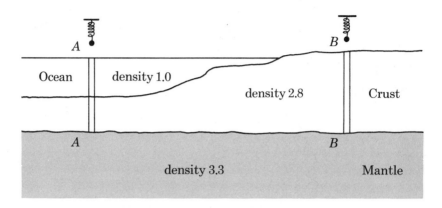

Figure 42. *If* the Moho were reasonably level between oceans and continents, then the continental column *BB* would contain more mass than an oceanic column *AA*. The gravitational attraction measured at the surface of the continent would therefore be greater than that measured at sea. The fact is that the attractions are nearly the *same* at the two locations; this model is evidently at fault.

picture. It indicates simply that, on average, there is the same mass of material below the ocean surface as below the continental surface. If, in Figure 43, the less dense crust under the ocean is thinner and the denser mantle is nearer the surface, it appears quite possible that the same mass could be contained in a vertical column down from the ocean as in a similar column of the continental structure, the oceanic deficiency in crust being balanced by an excess of mantle. If this were so, the gravitational attraction would be very nearly the same above the ocean as it is on the continents, as indeed is observed.

This balance is precisely what one would expect if the continents were literally floating on the mantle. Let us suppose that they are. At a given depth, say *A–B* in Figure 43, the pressure is the same, so that the total weight in each vertical column is also the same. In the column to the left, we know the density and depth of the ocean, the density (2.8) and depth of the oceanic crust. In the one on the right, the density and depth of

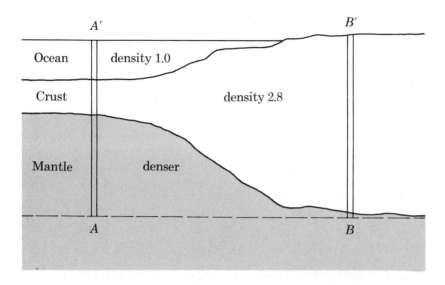

Figure 43. Below the continents, the denser mantle is depressed, so that the same mass is contained in the vertical columns *AA'* and *BB'*. In fact, knowing the densities of the ocean and the crust and the degree of depression of the continental Moho (from seismic evidence) the density of the mantle can be calculated to be approximately 3.2. This answer is consistent with the value of 3.3 found earlier in another way.

the continental crust are known. The only unknown is the density of the mantle material on which the crust 'floats,' but the equality of the weights in the two columns enables us to calculate this. If the balance is made and the figures given substituted, one finds that the density of the mantle material must be about 3.2—quite close to the value mentioned earlier. This agreement suggests that there may indeed be some element of truth in this simple picture!

This notion of 'floating continents,' the apparent balance between the weights of the oceanic and continental columns, is called *isostasy;** it is an effect whose ramifications extend far.

---

* A hybrid word. Greek *isos* = equal; Latin *stare* = to stand.

Yet it raises problems. We already know that the mantle is not an ordinary fluid since it is at least rigid enough to be the site of earthquake fractures at depths far below the Moho. Yet, the existence of isostasy is of the greatest importance—though it may be difficult to see all of its ramifications, it provides evidence that must be fitted in when the time comes to construct a detailed model of the crust and mantle.

4.6 THE CORE OF THE EARTH

The material of which the mantle is composed, though it may yield and flow under the loads imposed by the continents, is rigid enough to allow the generation of earthquakes and to allow the passage of S waves. The travel-time measurements described earlier allow the speeds c_p and c_s of P and S waves to be calculated for paths that penetrate deeper and deeper into the interior. Even when the maximum path depth is greater than 700 km (the greatest observed depth of deep focus earthquakes), the S waves can propagate without hindrance, so that the material is undoubtedly rigid insofar as these waves are concerned. However, beyond a depth of 2900 km (a radius of 3500 km from the center of the earth) there is an abrupt change. There appears to be a 'shadow' zone—the direct passage of S waves, even from intense earthquakes, is not observed at all at stations near the antipodes, the opposite point on the earth. There appears to be a region, the core, that is opaque to S waves, though not to P waves. The most obvious explanation of this fact, keeping in mind the properties of the two types of waves, is that the region inside a 3500 km radius is *liquid*. Moreover, it is found that both kinds of waves can reflect at the surface of this region to produce echoes at the surface of the earth; as in our interpretations connected with the Moho, this implies that the change is moderately abrupt, that there is another 'discontinuity,' separating what is apparently a liquid core from the more rigid mantle.

Is this core possibly the heart of iron about which we speculated in a previous chapter? If it is liquid, it must necessarily be very hot. We have no evidence yet about the temperatures inside the earth so that the question of whether or not this notion is consistent with other observations and inferences will have to be deferred. From the information that we have now, there is no way of telling whether the discontinuity from solid to liquid also coincides with a change in chemical composition. It may or may not; it is conceivable that the same material should exist on either side of the discontinuity, in the solid form above and the liquid form below, as it does at the bottom of a floating iceberg with ice above and water below. On the other hand, nothing definitely excludes a change in the type of material, as well as a change in state. There have been speculations on both sides, but the question remains open.

Not only does the speed of S waves drop abruptly to zero at the surface of the core (as Figure 38 illustrates) but the speed of P waves changes as well. The seismic measurements indicate that it drops suddenly to about 60% of its value at the bottom of the mantle. This, too, is consistent with the idea of a liquid core, for if the shear modulus e_s vanishes below the discontinuity, then, according to our previous formula for the speed of P waves, c_p, this should decrease also, even if the bulk modulus e_c is unaltered.

The seismic evidence for the two principal discontinuities— the Moho and the mantle-core boundary—have been observed many times; the results are consistent and reasonably unambiguous. There *may* be other discontinuities of one kind or another, but the observational evidence is often more equivocal. There *may* be some kind of transition zone, probably rather gradual, possibly a change in material, somewhere in the neighborhood of 900 or 1000 km below the surface. There *may* be a solid inner core at the very heart of the molten outer one; there are some seismic echoes that might be interpreted in this way. But the evidence is hardly compelling—these questions also remain open.

We are now in a very much better position than before to infer something about the actual distribution of mass inside the earth, of density with depth. Remember the constraints: the average density is known, the mass and volume; the moments of inertia are known, and we reason that the density cannot decrease with increasing depth. Added to this now is the distribution of wave speeds with depth—inferred fairly directly from travel-time measurements—from which we can calculate simply the *ratios* of elastic moduli to density (though not the two quantities separately). The problem is still not quite determinate yet—it requires more than just mathematics to obtain a single, unambiguous answer. The ambiguity is of the same kind that we found in our preliminary model at the end of the last chapter. We have more information now, but more unknowns, such as the variations of elastic moduli with depth. A model must still be constructed with both hypothesis and judgment; it must be analyzed and subjected to all the constraints available. Two such models have been constructed by K. E. Bullen in Australia; the density distributions that he found for these two models are shown in Figure 44. One postulates a solid inner core; the other does not. An interesting property of these models is that over much of the depth, the calculated densities are not very different. If different assumptions lead to almost the same result, then possibly the result is not crucially dependent on the assumption in detail, and even if neither is 'true' for the earth, perhaps the density distribution actually present is not very different from those calculated from the models. But this is something of a pious hope, not more; it is no deduction, no theorem, no logical consequence.

Sometimes, very intense earthquakes can set the whole earth into vibration, like a bell or a drop of water hanging from a faucet. Two, in particular, one in Chile in 1960 and one in Alaska in 1964 have been strong enough to cause the earth to 'ring' for many days. Sensitive seismographs have measured the tiny and slow oscillations of the whole earth that followed these events— the periods observed range from a few minutes to about an hour. Now the earth, like a bell or a violin string, has many types of possible oscillation, each of which has its own frequency and periodic time. Two kinds are shown in Figure 45. There are 'water drop' oscillations, in which the earth alternately stretches and contracts along (say) its polar axis and simultaneously shrinks and bulges at the equator. There are others that resemble a girl 'twisting,' in which the northern hemisphere rotates one way while the southern rotates in the other. Each of these (and of the many more complex types) has its own frequency and the job of associating a seismograph frequency with a particular

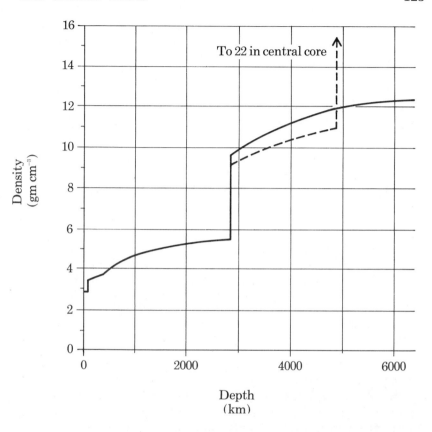

Figure 44. The density distribution in the earth according to Bullen's models. The solid line represents the result calculated with the assumption that the density varies smoothly except at the Moho and the mantle-core boundary. The broken line shows the modification when one assumes a solid central core whose density is (rather arbitrarily) taken as 10 gm/cc greater than that of the liquid core.

mode is not always easy. Nevertheless, free oscillations of the earth offer a potentially powerful means of discovering more about this problem, one that is only beginning to be understood. When compared with ordinary seismic waves, these low fre-

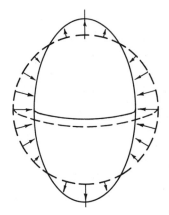 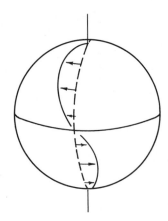

Figure 45. Two of the types of vibration of the earth as a whole. On the left is a 'water drop' vibration mode in which one axis alternately stretches and shrinks and on the right is a twisting mode in which the northern and southern hemispheres shake in opposite directions.

quency oscillations frequently involve gravitational restoring forces that are relatively much more important than those of elasticity, so that the frequencies observed are sometimes directly related to the distribution of density with depth in the earth. If one takes a model for the earth, with an *assumed* distribution of density and elastic constants, then the frequencies of the various modes of oscillation can be calculated. It is found, rather interestingly, that the density distribution inferred by Bullen and shown in Figure 44 gives results that agree reasonably well with the observed frequencies.

At first sight, this might be claimed as a triumph for the model, since it has predicted accurately a phenomenon that is quite independent of the information used to construct the model. However, it appears that the oscillation frequencies do not, in fact, depend closely on the details of the model assumed—the density distribution can vary a good deal without influencing the frequency very seriously; almost any sensible model will do. This is in a way unfortunate, since it demands a much higher precision in observation and a greater attention to small differences before a clear discrimination can be made between alternative models. One question that is still unsolved is this: if the frequencies of all the oscillation modes are measured precisely, can one work backwards and calculate the density distribution? The answer, I suspect, is no, not without further assumptions. But this is a frontier of present research, and the question may not remain unsolved for long.

5

Volcanoes: the Temperature inside the Earth

5.1 VOLCANIC ERUPTIONS

At the very least, the existence of volcanoes indicates that the interior of the earth is hot. This much is obvious—the evidence is of a most dramatic and direct kind—but it is perhaps less obvious how the study of volcanoes is the beginning of a chain of observation and inference that bears upon questions such as the nature of the deep interior, the possible movements of the continents and the origin of the earth itself.

There are about 450 active volcanoes in the world today and many more that appear to be dormant. Over half (some 280) lie around the borders of the Pacific Ocean as is shown in Figure 46; along the Andes of South America, the Sierra Madre of Central America, the Cascade Mountains in the northwestern United States, Alaska, Kamchatka, Japan, through Indonesia and New

Figure 46. The distribution of active volcanoes.

Guinea to the Solomon Islands. There are groups in Italy, in Iceland, in Africa and in Antarctica. A comparison between this map and the one (Figure 23) showing earthquake zones, is most revealing. Although there may not be any direct connection between a particular earthquake and a volcanic eruption, it is evident that the regions of the earth most prone to earthquakes are the ones in which volcanoes are most frequent. In general the two go together. This does not of course imply any 'cause and effect' relation, but it does suggest that both may be manifestations of some underlying process or mechanism that itself produces the unease and disquiet of these, rather than of other, parts of the earth's crust.

The most famous volcanoes are the ones known in antiquity: Vesuvius, Stromboli and Etna. The first of these destroyed half of Pompeii in 63 A.D. and engulfed the town completely sixteen years later. Stromboli rises from the sea, an almost perfect cone, constantly uneasy. From the Straits of Messina can be seen the pall of Etna, a long low cloud resting on the mountains of western Sicily. In the new world, in 1943, a fissure opened in a farmer's field in Michoacan, Mexico, and smoke and hot debris began to issue forth. By the end of a week, a volcanic cone, a pile of cinders 400 feet high had accumulated and at the end of a year a mountain, Paricutin, had been born. Some volcanoes are dormant for many years. Mount Rainier near Seattle, Washington, is believed to have had its last major eruption about 1410 A.D.; Mount St. Helena, some fifty miles south, was seen to erupt in 1843 by John C. Fremont, an explorer, who reported that the snows became black and ash fell as far as fifty miles away. Crater Lake, in Oregon, fills the cavity left by a huge volcanic eruption in prehistoric times; geologists believe that a mountain some 12,000 feet high once stood there. The largest explosion of recent times was in 1883 at Krakatoa, an island in Indonesia. A good part of the island disappeared in the blast and 36,000 lives were lost. The disturbance produced a wave in the atmosphere—not unlike a tsunami in the ocean (Section 4.1)—which reverberated round and round the world. The dust thrown into the sky was carried far by the wind and reddened the sunset for months thereafter.

Volcanoes, such as these, provide clues about the nature of the interior of the earth. Yet, as we shall see, these clues are only a beginning.

The simplest questions that we might ask are these: What comes out of a volcano? Where does it come from? The first appears easy to answer—one need merely collect a number of samples large enough to be reasonably representative and then analyze them. Though this is easy in conception, it requires little imagination to appreciate that in practice the process may be both arduous and hazardous, as well as subject to considerable uncertainty. Such studies have been made, however, and it appears that the magma—the molten rock below the surface—contains considerable steam and gas, mainly carbon dioxide, besides lava, the material that emerges as liquid and subsequently solidifies. Lava may appear in many forms. If the eruption is relatively slow, the lava may flow for miles, the bottom of the tongue cooling and solidifying as it rests on the ground with the molten top sliding over it. As the flow ceases, the whole mass solidifies; the surface may be on occasion smooth or in other places as rough and broken as clinker. If the eruption is explosive, the gas bubbles cause the lava to froth like champagne as it either overflows or shoots out in a fountain. As the frothy mixture cools and hardens, it falls as pumice (a rock so porous that it will commonly float on water) or as small rock particles known to vulcanologists as 'cinders' or 'ash.'

But where do the gases and the steam come from? The most likely answer, drawn from our background experience, is that they were always there, dissolved in the magma under very great pressure at the depths from which it came. Before one opens a bottle of soda water, there are no bubbles in the water; the gas is all dissolved. It is only when the bottle is opened and the pressure released that the bubbles form. In the same way, as the magma rises up the core of the volcano, the pressure drops and the bubbles of gas and steam probably form then.

It is not always easy to measure with accuracy the proportion of gas and steam in magma, but the solidified material can be analyzed in a geological or chemical laboratory. Perhaps the most interesting thing about the solidified lava is simply that there is nothing very dramatic about it. It varies, of course, but in general it is not very different from the other igneous rocks common on the earth's surface that were laid down in ages past. We can draw two clear inferences from this. In the first place, it would appear that these old igneous rocks, being so similar to modern lava, are themselves the result of volcanic activity when the earth was younger—one particular but very common type, basalt, being almost unmodified since it solidified. Secondly, at the depth from which the magma comes (whatever it may be) at least *some* of the material is, though perhaps molten, of a constitution similar to the igneous rock at the earth's surface. But how much of the material is like this? How representative is the magma of the material at the depth from which it comes? These are questions that we cannot yet answer; there is no way of telling. The magma *may* be squeezed out of a matrix like water from a sponge or milk from the udder of a cow; how can one say what the udder or the sponge is like by looking only at the liquid that comes forth? Or *is* the magma like the toothpaste from a tube, a reasonably fair sample of what is inside? On the face of it, the second alternative seems untenable. For one thing, magma is molten. Yet the *liquid* core of the earth, beyond the depth of 2500 km, is composed of rather dense material possibly containing much iron, and is certainly very different from the magma that comes from volcanoes. Wherever magma does come from, it is apparently not from the earth's core. The mantle, below the Moho, is predominantly solid, at least insofar as it allows the passage of S waves, so that *it* cannot consist of molten magma.

Nevertheless, there is one property common to most materials, including rock, that demands that this alternative be taken seriously. Unlike ice, most materials expand on melting. Ice is an exception and in some respects a paradox: the water into which it melts is *more* dense than it was in the solid form, so that ice floats on water. For most materials, the opposite is true; they expand on melting and the solid phase sinks through the liquid. It is not difficult to see in general why this should be so. The molecules in a solid are packed closely; each molecule remains more or less at the same point in the material and the whole matrix of atoms form a structure with rigidity, held together by the balance of inter-atomic forces. A crystal is a solid in which the arrangement of atoms forms an extremely regular lattice, not just over atomic distances, but over distances that can be seen easily with the eye. In all solids, the atoms vibrate about their average position even though they are not free to wander; it is in fact this vibration that gives them their temperature. The more heat energy added, the greater is the energy of atomic vibration and the higher the temperature. If so much heat is added that the vibration energy is sufficient to overcome the binding forces in the lattice, the atoms may escape from their places and begin to wander. As more and more atoms do this, the rigid structure dissolves and the material melts. In the molten state, the atoms and molecules are no longer closely packed but slide loosely amongst one another in an endless agitation. In this state they are not as compact as in the solid; one would expect the density, the overall mass per unit volume to be less. Water, as noted above, is one among few exceptions and the reasons for this are apparently not simple.

Liquids, then, generally contract when they solidify. Suppose now that we have a liquid just above its melting point, and apply a very great pressure to it. In melting, the atoms have just managed to escape from their lattice positions and spread out a little: one might guess that by applying sufficiently great pressure to a molten material we could force the atoms into close proximity again so that they would resume their places and solidify even though the temperature of the material (and energy of the atomic motions) was the same. And indeed this is so. It takes considerable pressure but the effect can be observed very easily in a laboratory. The melting point increases with pressure.*

The opposite process is the one that is immediately relevant to our speculation about volcanoes. Deep in the earth the pressure is very great and the melting point of the material is higher than it is at the surface. It is conceivable that the magma may be solid at the depth of origin; if the pressure drops, either by a partial venting in an earthquake fault, or by a movement of the loads that relieves some of the pressure, it may melt and escape upwards, *even though the temperature remains the same*—provided the pressure drop is sufficient to bring the melting point below the actual temperature of the material.

The second alternative, then, cannot be dismissed out of hand, but neither is it proven. The magma *might* be a fair sample of the material at its depth of origin, but again, it might not. The magma may be merely the constituent of a mixture or a porous structure that happens to melt at a temperature lower than does the rest. The measurements on the density of the magma are not very decisive. The average is found to be just less than three times the density of water, more dense than the average of the surface material but a little less than the values (3.2 or 3.3) calculated in Section 4.5 for the top of the mantle.

Finally, how hot is the lava? This can be measured directly. An optical pyrometer is an instrument that uses the color of a glowing body to measure its temperature; it is used commonly to measure the temperature of a furnace. A small filament is heated with electrical current and its color compared with that of the furnace. At about 600° C, a material glows dull red; at 1100° C, it is yellowish; and at 1500° C, it is white hot. The cur-

---

* So too, does the boiling point of liquids, for similar reasons.

rent running through the filament is adjusted until the color is the same as that of the furnace or the lava, and its temperature is then measured electrically. By observations of this kind, it is found that the temperature of emerging lava is generally about 1100° C, though it may be as cool as 1000° C or as hot as 1250° C.

5.2 THE STRUCTURE OF VOLCANOES

It now becomes crucial to discover from what depth the magma comes. The material itself has offered little evidence except that it is most unlikely to be from the earth's core. The only measurements that appear to offer a definite answer are seismic ones.

It is, in fact, commonly observed that seismic disturbances are associated with volcanic eruptions. The intensities are usually not great, but certainly sufficient to be recorded at a series of neighboring observation stations so that the methods described in Section 4.4 can be used to establish the location and depth of the disturbance. A number of such measurements have been made, and it is found that the depths of the seismic disturbances at the time of a volcanic eruption are surprisingly small—generally only 30 km or so. This is rather *less* than the depth of the Moho under the continents!

There are several matters that should be kept in mind while we explore the consequences of this finding. The first is that the seismic disturbances appear to be directly associated with volcanic eruptions, but we cannot infer from this any cause and effect relation. Most volcanic eruptions have associated seismic disturbances, but many earthquakes appear to have nothing to do with volcanoes at all. It *is* possible that the seismic disturbance associated with a volcano is in fact the trigger that sets off the eruption. One might imagine that the magma below the volcano is quiescent but unstable, rather like the champagne in a bottle that has been opened carefully. If the bottle is jogged, the gas may begin to come out of solution, and once this process begins, it accelerates; the bubbles grow rapidly and the champagne begins to foam out of the bottle. In the same way, if the magma is in an unstable state, a small seismic disturbance may be sufficient to initiate the release of gas and steam which breaks through the solid shell above and the volcano erupts. It is equally possible that the seismic disturbances may be simply a side-effect, produced by fractures and cleavages as the magma, already rising, forces its way to the surface. It is not yet possible to decide which if either of these models is the correct one; the most that we can say is that the two effects appear to be associated.

In the second place, the depth at which the seismic disturbance is observed is not necessarily the same as the depth from which the magma comes. If the first of the possibilities described above were to be valid, then one might expect that the two depths would be nearly the same. The intensity of seismic waves decreases, of course, with distance from the source. A quiescent but unstable region of magma may not be triggered by the weak seismic waves from a distant disturbance, but only by the more intense shock from a neighboring one; if this were the case, only those shocks near the region of magma would set off the instability. On the other hand, if the disturbances were produced by the rising magma forcing its way upwards, then the source of the magma would necessarily be rather deeper than the source of the seismic disturbances. Nevertheless, the differences may not be very great; there is little reason to suppose that seismic disturbances would be produced by the magma *only* after it has risen a considerable way. In summary, then, it is only with caution that we can identify the depth of about 30 km of the seismic disturbances as a rather rough indication of the depth of origin of the magma.

If we do take this step, however, it would appear that volcanic magma comes from the neighborhood of the Moho, either from the bottom of the crust or the top of the mantle. At this depth, magma could well be ordinarily solid, as has already been mentioned. From the magma 'deposit,' either one or a series of faults (or chimneys) reaches upwards toward the volcanic cone, as is shown in Figure 47. In the dormant state, these are filled with solidified magma; in an eruption the molten material forces its way up along a line of weakness to the crater, either the principal one or possibly a secondary crater in the vicinity. At one time, geologists believed that the upper mantle around the whole

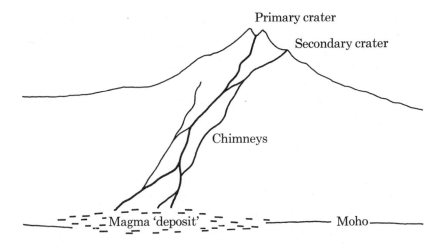

Figure 47. A simple sketch of the possible internal structure of a volcano.

earth consisted of a layer of molten magma but the seismic evidence—the apparently free passage of S waves through this region—forced them to abandon this idea. The model, devised initially to account for the existence of volcanoes, had to be discarded on the discovery of new evidence with which it was incompatible.* *If* the magma is molten at its depth of origin, then such regions are necessarily rather local and restricted in distribution to the volcanic zones of Figure 46. If, on the other hand, it is solid, then it *may* be distributed widely at this depth around the world, but for some reason or other it is perhaps rather hotter in these zones and more prone to instability. Some indication of why volcanoes (whatever the details of their structure) should, like earthquakes, occur in zones rather than being scattered widely about the earth's surface will emerge in the next chapter.

It is apparent, then, that our detailed knowledge of the workings of volcanoes is very sketchy. There is very little firm ob-

---

* This is an example of the inductive process described in Chapter 1.

servational evidence of a kind that could characterize many different volcanoes. Conjectures, ideas and suppositions abound, but little has emerged on which to base a detailed mathematical model of volcanic activity, that could be judged on the basis of its predictions. This situation is in direct contrast to the one that faced Newton in his contemplation of the planetary motions. He had detailed and reliable astronomical data in great quantity; he had Kepler's empirical laws, into which they had already been distilled. In our consideration of volcanoes, the observations are fewer and probably influenced by many different physical and chemical processes. Our understanding, even empirically, is of a most rudimentary kind and a detailed model is hardly in sight.

If, however, a model were to be developed, of what would it consist? Presumably, it would incorporate some representation of the temperature structure in the upper layers of the earth, some specification of the physical and chemical properties of the material to be found there and of the way that they change in time; these, together with a boldness of imagination and an economy of hypothesis. To be at all successful, it would have to predict such independently observable properties as, for example, the frequency of eruption and the energy released in an eruption and possibly some relation between the two. There is doubtless some element of chance or probability involved. One would expect such a model to predict, say, that a certain volcano is likely to erupt once in a hundred years and another once in ten years; it certainly could not say that Mount Rainier will erupt in fifty years and thirty days from now. It may provide relations between the known properties and some other ones which have not yet been measured but which could be; if such a connection were subsequently found by observation, it would represent a most significant achievement for the theory, and our credence in it would increase accordingly. But this is for the future; no such theory yet exists.

Nevertheless, the observations that have been made do have one very suggestive aspect. Let us combine the temperature measurements with the information from seismic sources on the depth of origin. We can take as representative figures, the temperature of 1100° C for the magma, 20° C for the average temperature of the surface rocks and 30 km as the depth of origin. As a first

approximation, let us suppose that the temperature of the emerging lava is the same as the temperature at the depth from which
it has come. This is pure supposition; on the one hand, it is conceivable that the magma may cool somewhat as it rises through
the core of the volcano but, on the other, it is equally conceivable
that chemical processes, involved in the release of the gas and
the steam could liberate heat and cause the temperature to rise.
At the present, we are unable to evaluate the relative importance
of these two possible effects which act in opposite directions;
our assumption supposes, in effect, that they roughly balance out.
The temperature difference between the region 30 km deep below a volcano and the surface is then $(1100 - 20) = 1080°$ C. If
the temperature changes with depth are relatively smooth, then
the average temperature gradient, the rate of change per unit
depth is

$$\frac{1080° \text{ C}}{30 \text{ km}} = 36° \text{ C per km,}$$

or $1°$ C per $1/36$ km; approximately $1°$ C per 30 m.

This is a very interesting figure, but one should not yet ascribe
too much significance to it. Remember all the assumptions and
approximations on which it is based—as in any calculation, the
more of these there are, the less reliable the answer is likely to
be. Remember, too, that this temperature gradient is inferred
from measurements in the volcanic zones *only;* one cannot immediately assume that the same temperature gradient would be
found in the regions of the earth that are not volcanically active.
Nevertheless, the figure is in some respects very surprising. It
implies that at a depth of just over 2 km, the temperature is
about $80°$ C above the temperature of the earth's surface, which
we took to be $20°$ C; at this depth the temperature is about
$100°$ C, the normal boiling point of water! At 30 km, the earth
is as hot as an ordinary industrial furnace.

If, without any justification, we were to assume that the *same*
temperature gradient persisted to the center of the earth, a depth
of 6400 km, the temperature there would be

$$T = 20 + (36 \times 6400)$$
$$= 230{,}000° \text{ C approximately.}$$

This answer is absurd—such a temperature is far hotter than

that of the surface of the sun, and if the center of the earth were as hot as this, the whole planet would explode. Clearly, something is grossly erroneous in at least one of our assumptions. The most suspect ones are first that the temperatures underneath volcanoes are characteristic of those to be found generally at the same depth, and secondly that the temperature gradient persists right to the center of the earth. The first of these is subject to independent investigation and the second to a much more critical scrutiny; to these we now turn.

5.3 THE HEAT FLOW FROM THE EARTH'S INTERIOR

The way in which the temperature of the earth increases with depth near the surface can be found in regions that are not volcanically active simply by drilling. It is not always necessary to drill for this purpose alone; there are many deep wells and a few deep mines in which such measurements can be made. The depths to which they extend are not great, usually only 5000 m or so, which is a tiny fraction of the earth's radius, and small even compared with the depth of the Moho. Nevertheless, there are many such drillings and they are scattered about the land surface of the earth much more widely than are the volcanic zones. The temperature gradients, the rates of increase of temperature with depth, measured in this way (Figure 48) vary to a considerable extent from one location to another, as might be expected from the geological variations. Gradients as small as 1° C per 140 m are measured in some locations and as large as 1° C per 10 m in others, but in spite of this, the average over many such drillings in many countries of the world is very close to 1° C per 30 m; the rate that we inferred from the volcanic measurements.

In some respects, this is quite surprising. There was little reason to believe that the temperature gradients measured in volcanic zones would be in essence the same as in other regions of the earth's surface and, indeed, fairly good reason to suppose that they would not. The very existence of volcanic regions implies an association with some kind of unusual and localized processes or properties. In spite of this, however, it now appears

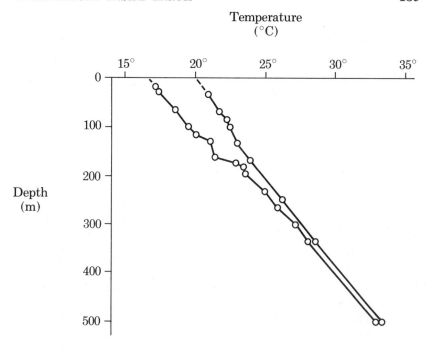

Figure 48. Distributions of temperature with depth in the upper part of the earth's crust, measured in California. The top series of connected points refers to a drilling made on land near the coast; the lower series to one offshore which penetrates the continental shelf. These results are in many ways characteristic of those found in deep wells in other parts of the world.

that the average temperature variation with depth is not one of these unusual properties—the temperature seems to increase at much the same rate as in volcanically quiet regions. Moreover, drillings into the ocean bed indicate that the temperature gradient there, too, is not very different from the same value, 1° C per 30 m. As we shall see later, this, again is rather surprising; recall that the Moho is very much higher and the crust thinner under the oceans than it appears to be under the continental land masses. If the temperature increases at about the same rate through the oceanic and continental crust, then since the crust is thinner beneath the oceans, the temperature at the Moho must be less there than it is under the continents. In fact, since the seismic evidence indicates that the oceanic crust is only about 6 km thick, then,

$$
\begin{matrix}
\text{Temperature at} \\
\text{oceanic} \\
\text{Moho}
\end{matrix}
=
\begin{matrix}
\text{Temperature at} \\
\text{bottom of} \\
\text{ocean}
\end{matrix}
+
\begin{matrix}
\text{Temperature} \\
\text{gradient}
\end{matrix}
\times
\begin{matrix}
\text{Crust} \\
\text{thickness,}
\end{matrix}
$$

and since the temperature of the water at the ocean bottom is just above $0°$ C, this gives

$$
0°\ C + \frac{1}{30} \times 6000 = 200°\ C,
$$

quite a lot less than the $1100°$ C or so found from the volcanic measurements, or calculated in a similar way from the same temperature gradient with a continental crust thickness of 30 or 40 km. This is a curious part of the puzzle whose significance is not yet clear, but which we shall have to keep in mind.

Now, in any solid body, a temperature gradient is associated with a flow of heat. A saucepan, filled with water, is on a lighted stove. The metal at the bottom of the saucepan on the outside is in contact with the hot gas from the flame; its temperature may be, say $400°$ C. Inside, it is in contact with the water; when this is simmering, the temperature of the metal in contact with the water is near the boiling point of water, $100°$ C. Through the bottom of the saucepan, then, there is a temperature difference, T, of $300°$ C; if the metal is 0.2 cm thick, the *temperature gradient* is the temperature difference divided by the thickness d,

$$
\frac{T}{d} = \frac{300}{0.2} = 1500°\ C \text{ per cm.}
$$

Because of this temperature gradient, heat flows through the bottom of the pan and into the water; the temperature of the water rises. There is a very simple relation between the flow of heat Q across an area A and this temperature gradient; for almost all materials it is found that they are proportional:

$$
Q \propto A \frac{T}{d}. \tag{5.1}
$$

This relation, which has been verified in many different laboratory experiments on solid bodies, has wide application; it is distinguished by the name 'Fourier's law of heat conduction,' in honor of J. B. Fourier (1768–1830), the French physicist and mathematician who discovered it. As in all proportional relations, it can be written as

$$Q = KA \frac{T}{d},$$ (5.2)

where K, the constant of proportionality, is a property of the material concerned, and A the area over which the heat flows. Materials for which K is relatively large conduct an appreciable amount of heat per unit area for a moderate temperature gradient T/d. These are the good conductors (copper, silver, aluminum). The materials for which K is much smaller conduct very little heat for the same temperature gradient; these are thermal insulators. It is natural that the constant K be called the *thermal conductivity*. The bottom of a saucepan should clearly be made of a material that conducts heat well, and it is evident why aluminum and copper are commonly used. Moreover, it should be only as thick as it must be for reasons of strength, so that a given temperature difference T produces as large a gradient T/d and so as large a heat flow as possible.

With these things in mind, then, it becomes apparent that the temperature gradient at the surface of the earth is associated with a heat flow up from the interior. This immediately raises the questions: How large is this heat flow? Whence does it come? Before we seek solutions to these problems, however, we must first establish rather more precisely and in greater detail what we mean by 'heat flow' and how it is measured.

Heat and temperature express two quite distinct ideas. Temperature is measured by a thermometer; it is a property associated with our sensations of 'hot' and 'cold,' just as the simple idea of weight is associated with the muscular effort required to lift something. The heat contained in a body, on the other hand, is an expression of the energy of molecular agitation.* Two bodies at the same temperature may contain different total amounts of heat. If one is more massive than the other, the total

---

* This is not a *definition* of heat; a precise definition would require a considerable digression into the laws of thermodynamics.

energy of agitation of all its molecules may be greater, simply because there are more of them; its total heat content is greater. Nevertheless, to *increase* the temperature of a body requires the addition of heat. Heat is therefore measured as the amount of energy needed to raise the temperature of a body by a certain amount. It is expressed (in metric units) in calories; 1 calorie is defined as the heat energy required to raise the temperature of 1 gram of *water* (very nearly 1 cubic centimeter) by 1 Centigrade degree.* If we have m grams of water, then we require m times as much heat to raise the temperature 1 degree; if the temperature rise is δT degrees,† then we require (δT) times as much heat. So, more generally, the amount of heat required to raise the temperature of m grams of water by δT degrees is

$$q = m \, \delta T.$$

Now, water is specified only by convention and not for any more fundamental reason. The same mass and the same temperature rise in another substance may require a different amount of heat. The quantity of heat is still proportional to m and δT, but may involve a further quantity C, a characteristic of the material, such that

$$q = Cm \, \delta T, \tag{5.3}$$

where C is called the specific heat of the material concerned. The specific heat of water is, according to the way in which the definitions have been set up, just unity; since, from the last equation,

$$C = \frac{q}{m \, \delta T}, \tag{5.4}$$

its units are calories per gram per centigrade degree. The specific heats of other materials can be measured by comparing the heat required to change the temperature of a given mass of the material by a certain amount and that required for the same mass of water; the branch of classical physics devoted to such matters is called calorimetry. The specific heat of iron is about 0.13 and that of basalt about 0.20 times that of water.

---

* More properly called, by international convention, 1 Celcius degree.
† See the footnote on page 35 concerning this 'delta notation.'

The heat flow Q over a surface is the rate of flow of heat energy across the surface; the amount that crosses per unit time. We have already seen that the heat flow can be expressed in Fourier's law of heat conduction, equation (5.2), in terms of the temperature gradient that causes the flow and the thermal conductivity K that characterizes the ability of the material to allow this. This is analogous to describing the flow of water through a pipe in terms of the pressure gradient forcing it along and the internal friction (determined by the cross-sectional area and inside surface roughness) that characterizes the resistance to flow along its length. We can express the flow of water more simply in terms of the amount that passes through in a given time, by the rate at which it fills a bucket at the end. In the same way, we can alternatively express the heat flow into a body in terms of the rate at which its heat content (and so temperature) rises. If Q is the rate of heat flow, which continues over a time interval t, then the total heat supply,

$$q = Qt,$$

or

$$Q = \frac{q}{t}. \tag{5.5}$$

Let us now apply these ideas to the question of the heat flux from the earth. The *heat flux* from the interior, the heat flow per unit area, can be found from Fourier's law in the form

$$\frac{Q}{A} = K\frac{T}{d}.$$

The temperature gradient (T/d) has been measured; its average value is 1° C per 30 m, or

$$\frac{T}{d} = \frac{1° \text{ C}}{30 \times 100 \text{ cm}} = 3.3 \times 10^{-4} \text{ °C per cm.}$$

The thermal conductivity* K for granite or basalt can be meas-

---

* It should be noted that since Fourier's law, equation (5.2), can be

ured in calorimetric experiments in the laboratory on geological specimens. The results are somewhat variable, of course, because of the inevitable variation in the exact nature of the rock specimens, but a representative value is

$$K = 6 \times 10^{-3} \text{ cal sec}^{-1} \text{ °C}^{-1} \text{ cm}^{-1}.$$

This, together with the temperature gradient T/d given above, indicates that the heat flow per unit area from the earth's interior is

$$\frac{Q}{A} = 6 \times 10^{-3} \times 3.3 \times 10^{-4}$$

$$= 2 \times 10^{-6} \text{ cal sec}^{-1} \text{ cm}^{-2}, \text{ nearly.} \tag{5.6}$$

Compared with the incoming radiation from the sun (about 4×10^{-3} cal sec^{-1} cm^{-2}), this heat flow is very small; it is an insignificant part of the heat budget of the world that we know, its oceans and atmosphere. Nevertheless, its existence is of the greatest importance to us in our search for the nature of the heart of the earth.

Where does the heat go? Unless the earth's surface is gradually, over the years, becoming hotter, it must be lost as rapidly as it is gained. The radiation from the sun is partially reflected by the earth and its atmosphere, and only partially absorbed. The heat seeping up is likewise absorbed by the oceans and atmosphere, and its identity is lost as it mingles with the solar energy supply. It is transformed from one form to another as it plays its part in the overall dynamics of the ocean and atmosphere, in the generation of hurricanes and ocean currents, but ultimately, it is re-radiated from the upper atmosphere into deep space, together, of course, with the much larger amount of heat absorbed originally from the sun.

---

rearranged to give

$$K = \frac{Qd}{TA},$$

then the units of K are given by

$$[K] = \left[\frac{Qd}{TA}\right] = \frac{\text{calories sec}^{-1}}{\text{°C}} \times \frac{\text{cm}}{\text{cm}^2} = \text{calories sec}^{-1} \text{ °C}^{-1} \text{ cm}^{-1}.$$

A more pertinent question is whence does it come? There seem to be two simple primary alternatives, which, in fact, are not mutually exclusive; each may contain part of the truth. The heat flow outwards through the surface of the earth means either that the earth is cooling down like a hot baked apple which will ultimately become cold and thermally inactive, or else that there is somewhere in the interior of the earth, a constant source of heat, a 'fire' that more or less balances the loss outwards and maintains the interior at a steady temperature. An evaluation of these alternatives is clearly of the utmost importance to us; let us begin by examining the first.

Let us suppose, then, that there is no internal generation of new heat inside the earth. One calculation that we can make is to find the time that it would take to cool the earth down with a heat flow outwards of the size that is observed. If this model is to be tenable, the answer must be consistent with everything else we can infer about the geological history of the earth. The chain of reasoning involved is quite similar to that used in the saucepan problem. Suppose that, in a time t the average temperature of the interior of the earth drops by an amount δT. From equation (5.3), the amount of heat lost when the temperature drops by this amount is

$$q = Cm\,\delta T,$$

where, here, C is the average specific heat of the earth and m the earth's mass. This amount of heat was lost in a time t, so that from equation (5.5), the rate of loss, the total heat *flow* outwards during the period was

$$Q_{\text{total}} = \frac{q}{t},$$

$$= \frac{Cm\,\delta T}{t}.$$

But the heat flux (Q/A), the flow per unit area, is just this quantity divided by the surface area of the earth, $4\pi\mathcal{R}^2$,

$$\frac{Q}{A} = \frac{Cm}{4\pi\mathcal{R}^2}\left(\frac{\delta T}{t}\right).$$

Hence, the rate of decrease of the earth's temperature, the temperature change divided by the time is given by

$$\frac{\delta T}{t} = \frac{4\pi \Re^2}{Cm}\left(\frac{Q}{A}\right). \tag{5.7}$$

On the right of this equation, the radius $\Re$ and mass m of the earth are known from Chapters 2 and 3, and the heat flux (Q/A) from equation (5.6). Only C, the average specific heat of the earth, is still unknown. Since only an approximate answer is needed, it will be sufficient to use a fairly rough estimate for C. It has already been mentioned that for basalt, $C = 0.20$ c.g.s. units and for iron, $C = 0.13$ c.g.s. units. Let us take, for the purposes of calculation, $C = 0.18$. Then in c.g.s. units throughout

$$Q/A = 2 \times 10^{-6} \text{ cal sec}^{-1} \text{ cm}^{-2},$$
$$m = 6.0 \times 10^{27} \text{ gm},$$
$$\Re = 6400 \text{ km} = 6.4 \times 10^8 \text{ cm},$$
$$C = 0.18 \text{ cal gm}^{-1} \text{ °C}^{-1}.$$

On substitution into (5.7),

$$\frac{\delta T}{t} = 0.95 \times 10^{-14} \text{ °C per sec,}$$

which seems astonishingly small. But there are $60 \times 60 \times 24 \times 365 = 3.16 \times 10^7$ seconds in a year, so that this corresponds to

$$\frac{\delta T}{t} = 0.95 \times 10^{-14} \times 3.16 \times 10^7$$

$$= 3 \times 10^{-7} \text{ °C per year, approximately,}$$

which is still very small. But the geological age of the earth, found in ways to be described at the end of this chapter, is several thousand million years; if the same heat flux had persisted throughout the last 1000 million years, the average temperature would have dropped by an amount

$$\delta T = 3 \times 10^{-7} \times 10^9$$
$$= 300° \text{ C,}$$

which does not seem absurdly large. Remember, however, that the surface temperature is governed predominantly by the energy balance with the sun's radiation; the upper atmosphere must be just hot enough to radiate the amount of energy that is absorbed from the sun. If the surface temperature has not changed greatly during this time, and the internal temperature, say at the Moho, was greater 1000 million years ago, then the temperature gradient was larger at that time; the rate of heat loss and the rate of cooling also larger than we have calculated. This means that we have, if anything, *underestimated* the temperature drop over the interval and that the internal temperature was at that time, if anything, rather higher than this.

Nevertheless, this first test of the model of simple cooling gives a result that does not seem to be inconsistent with the information that we have to date. If it had predicted a rate of cooling of 1° C per year, or even of 10^{-3} °C per year, the idea could have been dismissed out of hand; the interior of the earth would by now be quite cold. This model could conceivably represent a good part of the truth, were it not for some other observations on the radioactivity of the surface rocks.

5.4 RADIOACTIVITY

The surface rocks of the earth are, to some extent, radioactive. They contain traces of unstable elements, which gradually but spontaneously decay, the atomic nuclei breaking up one after the other and giving off small energetic particles which heat the surrounding material as they are slowed down. The most important of these unstable elements in the earth are uranium which decays into radium and lead, and thorium which also after decay becomes lead. Not all of the atoms in a given block of radioactive material break up at the same time, but in a certain time interval a certain fraction will undergo transformation. The number of radioactive atoms then decays gradually in time as shown in Figure 49. An important characteristic of each radioactive element is the *half-life*, which is defined as the time that one must wait until half the original atomic nuclei in the specimen have broken up. The half-lives of different radioactive materials vary tremendously—some are only a tiny fraction of a second, the nuclei being very unstable, while others are millions of years. Those that occur naturally in the earth are, of course, only those with very long half-lives—more unstable elements will have decayed long ago and completely disappeared during the earlier history of the earth. The half-life of uranium is about 5000 mil-

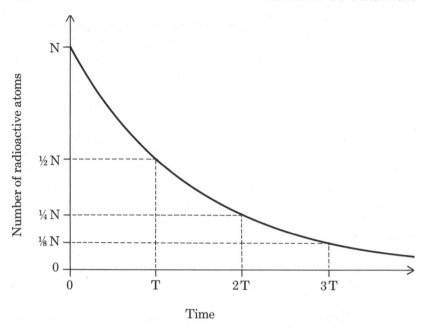

Figure 49. The decay of radioactive elements. The half-life T is the time that it takes for half the original number of radioactive atoms to decay. In one further half-life, half the remaining atoms decay, so that only one-quarter are left. After three half-lives, only one-eighth remain.

lion years, for thorium, 14,000 million years, so that any of these materials present when the earth was formed would, by now, have only partially decayed. But the decay, slow as it is, continues, liberating heat as it does so and constituting a kind of 'fire' that heats the interior of the earth.

If observations on the radioactivity of surface rocks are any indication, then, there seems to be a source of heat in the earth regardless of any tentative conclusion we might have drawn from the simple cooling model described at the end of the last section. The crucial question, of course, is how intense is this heat source? How much of the heat flow to the surface does it provide and how much comes from the cooling of the interior?

The rate of heat generation per unit volume of rock cannot be measured directly—it is far too small—but one can measure by careful analysis the proportion of each element in the rock and then, in a separate experiment, the rate of heat generation by decay of the pure element. The answer that we seek is then the product of these two numbers; it is found that in the sedimentary rocks of the earth, the rate of generation is about 2×10^{-13} cal cm^{-3} sec^{-1}, for granite about 4×10^{-13}, and for basalt approximately 1×10^{-13} cal cm^{-3} sec^{-1}. A most interesting aspect of these numbers is that the result found for granite (a representative constituent of the crust above the Moho) is four times as large as for basalt, which is probably more like the deeper material below the Moho. They suggest immediately that the rate of heat generation is a good deal greater above the Moho than it is below; that the 'fire' is not concentrated deep in the heart of the earth but is an encircling sheet near the surface itself!

This suggestion is reinforced by a simple calculation that makes use of these observations together with the earlier measurement of the surface heat flux. We do not know in detail how the radioactive heat generation is distributed with depth; let us suppose for the sake of calculation that above the Moho, heat is generated throughout the material at the rate measured in granite, and that *no* heat is generated below. What fraction of the observed heat flow would be associated with this distribution of heat sources? The depth of the Moho is about 35 km, and each cubic centimeter of the material above is producing heat at the rate 4×10^{-13} cal per second. A column, from the surface to the Moho, 1 square centimeter in cross-section, will generate

$$Q_r = 4 \times 10^{-13} \times 35 \times 10^5 \text{ cal/sec,}$$

since there are 10^5 cm in each km. This gives

$$Q_r = 1.4 \times 10^{-6} \text{ cal/sec,}$$

and in steady conditions, this must flow outwards through the surface. The total measured heat flux is about 2×10^{-6} cal/sec per square centimeter; evidently these radioactive sources could account for as much as 70% of the total. If there is, in addition, some radioactivity below the Moho, it is quite apparent that the addition of the heat generation there to the figure above could easily account for the entire surface heat flux measured!

These considerations, then, force us to abandon the idea of a gradually cooling earth without heat generation, in spite of the fact that the 'cooling time' was not, on the face of it, either absurdly short or absurdly long. The model that emerges is one in which the internal temperature of the earth is governed largely by the generation of heat in the earth's crust and possibly a little below it. This generation may not *exactly* balance the heat flow outwards through the surface; if the present generation rate is slightly less than the outwards flux, then the average temperature of the interior may be decreasing very gradually, at a rate slower than the one we calculated in the previous section, since part of the heat loss is offset by the internal generation. On the other hand, the generation may be rather in excess of the present rate of loss; in that event the interior is gradually becoming hotter. There is at present no way of telling with certainty which of these alternatives is the correct one; each possibility has its advocates.

This general conclusion of a shallow heat source provides a solution to another part of the puzzle that we encountered earlier. It was pointed out that the temperature gradient measured at the surface could not possibly continue to the center of the earth, since this would lead to absurdly high temperatures there. Suppose, for the sake of discussion, we again take a definite model; that all the heat is generated in a layer near the surface and that this exactly balances the measured surface heat flux—the interior is at a steady temperature, neither heating nor cooling. Since there is no temperature change in the interior, then there is no *net* heat flux there either, and from Fourier's law, there is *no temperature gradient*. The internal temperature, below the depth of the heat source, is quite uniform. This model is exactly analogous to the inside of a furnace that is heated by elements on all sides. The temperature at all points *inside* the furnace is the same; outside the elements, however, (toward the surface) the temperature drops rapidly through the walls to room temperature as the heat leaks out. For the earth, this simple model indicates that the relatively rapid temperature gradient found near the surface, continues only to the depth over which the radioactive sources are present and beneath that, the temperature is, in essence, constant. We know that at 30 km the temperature is about 1100° C; if the 'heating elements' are all above this, the temperature throughout the mantle and core is the same.

One should not, however, expect this simple picture that we have postulated to be literally exact. There may be *some* degree of radioactivity at great depths even in the core of the earth, so that the deep temperature gradient, though small, may not be exactly zero. Nevertheless, the fact remains that *most* of the radioactive decay appears to be concentrated near the surface, so that the temperature of the core of the earth, if not as small as 1100° C, may be, say, 3000° C (Figure 50), but almost certainly not, say, 10,000° C.

In summary, then, it appears that this description draws together most of the quantitative observations that we have on the temperature and heat flux from the earth's interior, and to this extent, it demands an element of credence. Nevertheless, some puzzles remain. Remember that the heat flux from the ocean bottom is found to be about the same as that from the continental land masses but that the thickness of the crust is much less. If the heat sources are restricted to the crust, and if (as seems reasonable) the radioactivity per unit crustal volume is the same below the oceans as in the continental land masses, then one would expect that the total heat generated in the oceanic crust would be considerably less and hence the heat flux upwards correspondingly less. This is contrary to observation—why? Again, why *should* the radioactive materials be concentrated in the surface layer? The elements involved are very dense; if the earth cooled from a liquid mass, one would expect them to settle to the center. But no: they are apparently found almost entirely at the surface—why? Convincing answers to these questions may one day be found; they will probably involve some new element of the model, which up to now, has not been considered.

5.5 THE ORIGIN OF THE EARTH

It has already become apparent that the thermal history of the earth, its constitution and the distribution of various mate-

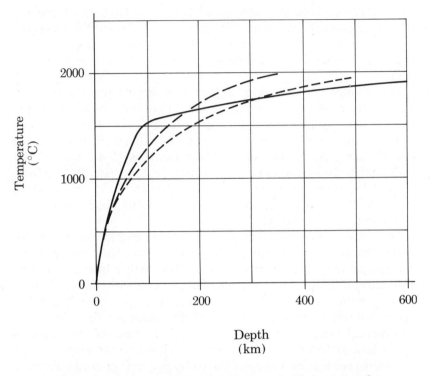

Figure 50. Temperature distributions in the crust and
upper mantle, calculated according to rather different
models. The solid curve was found by Gutenberg; the
broken ones by MacDonald for regions under the ocean
(the upper curve) and under the continents (lower).
The differences between these curves give some idea
of the uncertainties involved.

rials with depth, are reflections of the way in which the earth
was formed. The contemplation of these matters has occupied
many of the great geophysicists and mathematicians of the last
hundred years, among them Poincaré, Jeans, Eddington, Jeffreys, Lyttleton and Hoyle, but no finality has been reached—
cogent objections have been raised for every model proposed.
The problem is one of enormous difficulty. We have only observational evidence on the present state of the earth and of the solar

system; from this, we must infer how it arose. The well-established laws of Newtonian mechanics provide both a guide and a straitjacket; certain manners of evolution can be traced out and others that might be conceived can be shown to be dynamically impossible. Moreover, the heat content of the earth and its generation must have been such that the temperature and heat flux is now what it is observed to be. Accounting must be made of the apparently different chemical constitutions of the planets and the way that they differ from that of the sun; of the different sizes and inclinations of their elliptic orbits and their rates of rotation about their respective axes. These are some of the problems; they are exciting of the imagination but demanding on the skills even of such scientific giants as these.

One piece of information of the greatest importance comes from geology: the time scale of the earth's history, or the time since the various rocks were formed. The *relative* ages of various rocks were established many years ago by observations on the layering of the earth's crust. In the absence of volcanic intrusions and overturning, the older rocks must generally lie beneath newer sedimentary ones. The same is not necessarily true of igneous rocks. If the earth began as a molten mass with a solid skin formed by cooling, and if the molten region contracted inwards as the skin thickened, then the most recently solidified rocks *may* be at the bottom, near the interface between the solid and liquid regions. But again, even this is not necessarily true: solidified material is usually denser than its liquid form—would not newly solidified material near the surface tend to sink through the melt? Anyway, as far as the sedimentary rocks are concerned, the situation is fairly clear, and they can be arranged rather unambiguously in order of relative ages.

The determination of the *actual* ages of rocks had to wait for this century and an understanding of the processes of radioactive decay. The presence of radioactive but long-lived elements in the earth has already been described, together with the fact that thorium, for example, decays to lead. If the rock, when formed, contained just thorium, then, as time went by and the thorium decayed to lead, the smaller would be the amount of thorium and the greater the amount of lead. The *ratio* of thorium to lead would then be a clear index of the time since the rock was formed. After one half-life of thorium, just half of the original material would have decayed, and there would be equal numbers of atoms of thorium and of the decay product, lead. After a further half-life, half of the *remaining* thorium would have decayed; there would then be only one part of thorium to three of lead. The half-life of thorium is measured in the laboratory by counting the very small proportion of atoms in a relatively pure specimen that decays in a certain time. When armed with this figure, we can, by assaying the relative abundance of thorium and lead in a rock specimen, calculate how much time has elapsed since its formation.

One real problem of course is that there is no guarantee that the rock did not contain some lead to begin with. If we could not distinguish between this and the lead formed by radioactive decay, the method would fail. Fortunately, it *is* possible; the decay product is a single particular isotope of lead with a characteristic nuclear mass while 'primordial' lead consists of a mixture of isotopes with slightly varying masses of the different atomic nuclei. The distinction between the two clearly requires sophisticated techniques of isotope separation, but it can be done and the amount of lead associated with radioactive decay can be determined unambiguously. A further check is given by the layering observed in field geology that indicates the relative ages; the actual ages must of necessity lie in the same ordering.

In this way, then, one can estimate the time that has elapsed since many of the surface rocks of the earth were formed. As we have already mentioned briefly, the answers turn out to be very large indeed—for the older rocks they are hundreds of millions of years. The earliest traces of life are found in fossil remains in rocks about 600 million years old; the age of the earth is probably about 4500 million years.

This, then, gives some idea of the time scale, of the kind of time interval involved since the earth was formed. But whence did it come? The search for the answer leads beyond geophysics to cosmology, the science of the cosmos itself; in it, there is no finality but much debate.

There appear to be three general alternative possibilities, none of which is free from serious objection. The first envisages a primordial catastrophe, a blazing gaseous sun disrupted by a collision or near encounter with another star that resulted in an extended trail or filament which subsequently cooled rapidly and condensed into the drops that became planets. Compared with the measured age of the earth, the time that it would take a gaseous blob with the mass of the earth to condense is very short. Jeffreys, one of the founders of modern geophysics, calculated that about 5000 years would suffice—the initial temperature being so high that the cooling rate would be very rapid indeed. A hot liquid earth would continue to cool rapidly and within possibly 10,000 years, the beginnings of a solid crust would form. Once this had happened, the cooling rate would decrease rapidly, and with the presence of internal radioactive heat sources, the presently observed thermal properties could easily result after the lapse of a further two or three thousand million years or so. Nevertheless, this 'catastrophic' theory faces fundamental difficulties. The masses of the planets together are a very small fraction of the mass of the sun, yet their distances from the sun are so great in comparison with the sun's diameter that their combined moment of inertia (Chapter 3, p. 72) is much larger than that of the sun—they possess nearly all of the angular momentum of the solar system. The dynamical problem has been to devise a type of collision that, while obeying the laws of Newtonian mechanics, would produce fragments with this property, and this has been a real stumbling block. Other problems arise from the composition of the planets. Not only does the distribution of elements in the composition of each planet differ from that of the sun (which is largely hydrogen) but it also appears to differ from one planet to another. There have been very serious attempts by many people to resolve these problems, but a good many remain.

Another general possibility advanced by the German astrophysicist von Weizsäcker and others, is that the sun was originally surrounded by a disc-like nebula, containing whorls and eddies which gradually coalesced and condensed to yield a series of orbiting planets. This model has been worked out in much less detail and so it is to a large extent untested; imagination has run ahead of our mathematical ability. It remains to be seen whether this picture will stand up to the cold evaluation necessary before it can be regarded seriously.

One further possibility, considered by Fred Hoyle, is that the planets were never hot gaseous masses, but were formed by the accretion or the collection of solid inter-stellar dust particles by small proto-planets. As a small solid mass moves through a dust cloud in space, it draws the dust particles toward it by its gravitational attraction. Some will collide, gradually increasing the original mass. The larger the planet becomes, the larger its gravitational attraction on the neighboring dust and the larger it grows. According to this model, the planets began by being cold and their interiors gradually became hotter on account of radioactive heat sources below the surface. As we saw in the case of the earth, the presence of these sources left open the possibility that the interior may be becoming hotter as the ages go by, so that this possibility is not obviously absurd. Nevertheless, once again, neither is it proven; the whole question is one of speculation.

None of these models is successful in the sense that it can predict the present number of planets, their sizes, orbits and constitutions. The problems are, however, of great difficulty; they will continue to excite and challenge the minds of men as long as we have the capacity to question and wonder.

6

Continental Drift?

6.1 FRAGMENTS OF CIRCUMSTANTIAL EVIDENCE

In the early days of this century, a German geophysicist, Alfred Wegener, advanced an idea that has become one of the most provocative and hotly debated in all of geophysics. In studying the map of the Atlantic Ocean, he became engrossed with the remarkable coincidence between the shapes of the coastlines on either side—they seemed to fit together like the pieces of a jigsaw puzzle. The bulge of North Africa fits neatly into the Caribbean and the coasts of Europe and North America both slope away to the northeast. The apex of Brazil fits into the bight of Africa at the Congo and the opposing coastlines to the south run nearly parallel. Unwilling to accept this as mere chance, Wegener made the bold suggestion that the two continental land masses were once united, that they fractured and over the ages have gradually drifted apart. To support this contention, he constructed an elaborate and rather fanciful 'theory' whose aim was to account in an inclusive way for a wide variety of observation, not only in geophysics, but in geology, paleontology, oceanography and climatology. The details of his description would strain the credulity of the least critical of modern geophysicists, but the primary fact remains; the coincidence is remarkable and has become even more so as further observational information has been uncovered.

The first type of evidence comes from descriptive geology. In considering the possible fit between the two continental masses, it is not quite fair to regard the modern coastlines as the edge of each. In geological terms, the continents do not end abruptly there, but extend below the shallow coastal seas, whose bed undulates at depths of one or two hundred meters and from which rise the offshore banks and islands. This continental shelf varies in width, being in some places (for example, off the coast of California) only 30 or 40 km wide and in others (as in the Arctic Ocean, north of Siberia) perhaps 400 km. Beyond it, the bottom slopes rather abruptly to the deep ocean bed, some 4000 m below the ocean surface. The continental slope really marks the edge of the land mass; one should compare the shapes of *these* on either side of the Atlantic rather than the shapes of the coastlines themselves. If one does this, as in Figure 51, the fit is, if anything, improved; it may not be quite so evident on a flat map, but if the fitting is done on a globe it is already quite persuasive. But that is not all: many old geological structures on either side seem to correspond like the lines of writing on a piece of paper that has been torn down the middle. Not only do the shapes of the pieces fit, but the lines also. For example, the Great Glen in Scotland between Inverness and Oban continues, when the shapes are fitted, as the Cabot Fault across Newfoundland and Nova Scotia. This is one example among quite a number; the correspondences have accumulated, item by item. Each one by itself could be pure chance, but as the number increases, the probability of their *all* being just chance becomes rather remote.

Newer evidence of a different kind has been found by the methods of radioactive dating described in the previous chapter. The continental rocks are thousands of millions of years old— this is the time elapsed since the rocks were formed, presumably from the molten state. Recently, with the advent of deep ocean sounding, it has been discovered that down the middle of the Atlantic Ocean, from Iceland in the north to Bouvet Island in the south, there extends a huge submerged mountain range, the Mid-Atlantic Ridge, a region seismically unsettled and geologically new. Some of the rocks here appear to be surprisingly young—it is a mere million years since they were solidified. Moreover, and even more surprisingly, the islands of the Atlantic on either side seem, according to the same dating methods, to be aged more or less in direct proportion to their distances from the Mid-Atlantic Ridge!

This last finding is a very important one. If we were to assume that the islands were formed from the Mid-Atlantic Ridge, it suggests that the crust has been tearing apart along this line and carrying the islands either to the east or to the west—that the islands and the continents on either side have been steadily separating. If this presumption is correct, and we divide the distance of each island from the Mid-Atlantic Ridge by its age, we have the average speed of movement. For most of the islands, it can be seen from Figure 52 that this comes out to be about 2 cm per year although, to be sure, there is a good deal of variability. Could this be the speed of the continental drift?

Such a speed is, of course, much too small to be measured directly. The measurement of oceanic distance involves such inaccuracies that even over historical times there is little chance of observing such small changes as this figure would suggest. Nevertheless, there were between 1920 and 1940 a number of inconclusive attempts to measure any significant changes in the distance between, for example, Greenland and Europe. In these earlier attempts, it was always most uncertain whether any differences that appeared to be found were not simply the result of observational error. The method involving radioactive dating is free of the demands of extreme accuracy in the measuring of oceanic distances and offers the first quantitative information on the relative speed of continental movements, but even so, we must continue to be cautious. The ages of the oceanic Atlantic islands are *more or less* proportional to their distances from the Mid-Atlantic Ridge, but not by any means exactly. This, again, could be pure chance, though our repeated appeal to chance is becoming rather bleak.

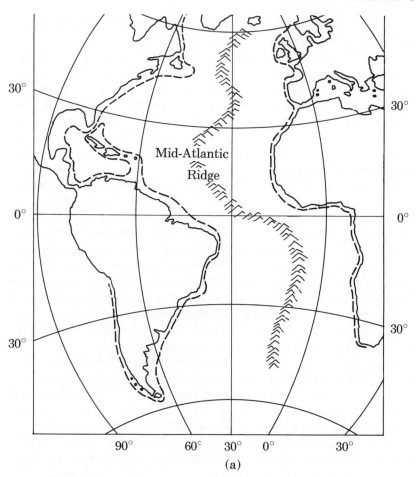

30°

30°

Mid-Atlantic
Ridge

0°

0°

30°

30°

90°   60°   30°   0°   30°

(a)

Figure 51 (a) and (b) *on facing page*. The fitting of
the coastlines on either side of the Atlantic Ocean. On
the left, the present continental positions are shown
with the Mid-Atlantic Ridge extending south from Iceland. The approximate edges of the continental shelves
are indicated by the broken lines surrounding the modern coasts. On the right, the continents are fitted together along the edges of their continental shelves. The
dotted line shows the Cabot fault in North America extending to the Great Glen in Scotland.

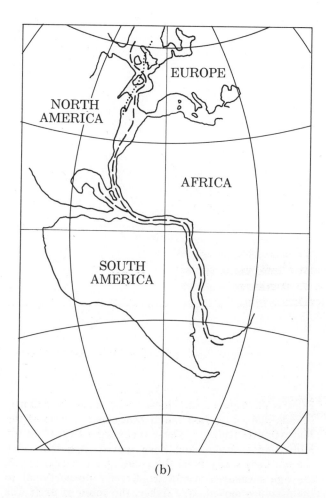

(b)

An even more suggestive piece of evidence comes from the study of rock magnetism in the vicinity of the Mid-Atlantic Ridge. The earth has a magnetic field and when rocks are formed either by magma cooling or by the consolidation of sediments, they are magnetized very weakly by the field of the earth. The direction of the rock magnetization corresponds to the direction of the earth's field at the time and place where they were formed —it is impressed on the nascent rocks and frozen in. It will be seen in the next chapter that the polarity, the direction of the

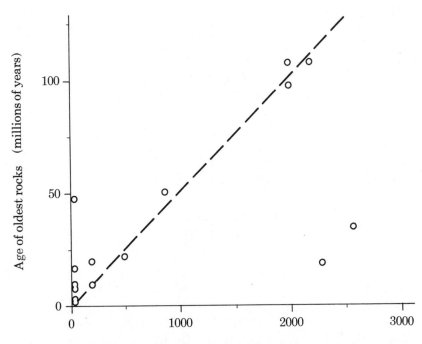

Figure 52. Ages of the oldest rocks found in Atlantic islands plotted against the distance east or west of the Mid-Atlantic Ridge. If these rocks were formed at the Mid-Atlantic Ridge and have moved (together with the sea bed) away from the ridge at a constant speed, the age measured would be directly proportional to the distance moved. If, further, the speed of drift was 2 cm/yr, the points would lie close to the broken line; the fact that they do suggests that this might be the speed of continental drift. The two points near the lower right hand corner are from Bermuda and the Canary Islands; these presumably have been formed more recently.

earth's magnetic field appears to have reversed occasionally in past ages. Thus, even if there were no continental movements, the directions of magnetization of successively older strata at any location would sometimes reverse, reflecting the directions of the earth's field at the times of their birth. These magnetically active regions in turn modify the primary field, producing small anomalies or local departures from the simple dipole* field.

Recent surveys of magnetic anomalies near the Mid-Atlantic Ridge have revealed a most remarkable pattern of reversals which, as Figure 53 shows, are very nearly symmetrical on either side. The pattern looks exactly as if the ocean floor were peeling apart along the line of the ridge, where new rocks are continually being formed. If, during one era, the earth's magnetic field is in a certain direction, the rocks that crystallize along the ridge will have the corresponding direction of magnetization. They gradually drift apart, to west or east. Then, perhaps, the direction of the earth's field is reversed; the magnetization of the new rocks along the ridge will now have the opposite polarity. The pattern would then consist of two stripes with the original polarity separated by the more recent rocks in which it is reversed. A continual tearing apart of the oceanic crust along this line with repeated reversals of the earth's magnetic field would produce a series of symmetrical striations in the pattern of magnetic anomalies just like the one found. These relatively new findings are probably the most persuasive of all—it is very difficult to conceive how this very clear pattern could have arisen in any other way.

There are many older fragments of information, much less clear, that suggest the possibility of past continental movements. Some of these also come from the study of rock magnetism combined with the techniques of radioactive dating. Rocks formed at the same time on different continents should have a consistent direction of magnetization, but if the continents have moved since the rocks were formed, this consistency would gradually be lost as the continents were rearranged. Observations on rocks of the same age from different continents do suggest relative

---

* See Section 7.1.

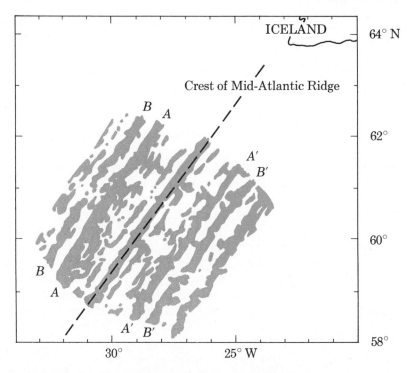

Figure 53. The pattern of magnetic anomalies over the
Reykjanes Ridge, part of the Mid-Atlantic Ridge south
of Iceland. The measurements were made by J. R.
Heirtzler, X. Le Pichon, and J. G. Baron. The dark
areas indicate regions of positive anomaly, in which
the underlying strata are magnetized in the same direction as the present magnetic field of the earth, and so
slightly augment the field. In the unshaded regions,
the anomaly is negative, the underlying rocks being
magnetized oppositely to the *present* field and so di-
minishing it slightly in these regions. Along the crest
of the ridge, the most recent rocks are magnetized in
the same direction as the present field. On either side,
there are striations apparently resulting from past
reversals of the earth's field, combined with a drift
outwards from either side of the crest. The general
symmetry of the bands *AA, A'A'* and *BB, B'B'* is
striking.

movements of this kind—it is very difficult to reconcile the observed directions of magnetization without continental movements. These observations do not indicate that Europe and America are gradually separating, but merely that some changes in their relative positions have occurred. Some other facts are suggestive but ambiguous. Coal has been found in Antarctica; either the earth was once so warm that vegetation flourished at the South Pole, or perhaps Antarctica itself was somewhere other than at the Pole. Furthermore, about 200 million years ago, when the southern continents were gripped in an ice-age, the geological dating methods indicate that coal deposits in Europe were being formed from tropical forests. Europe is no longer near the equator; perhaps the axis of spin of the earth has changed, or again, perhaps the continents have drifted.

This is the kind of evidence that forms the case for continental drift. It is circumstantial in the sense that none of it is *proof;* many of the individual items can be 'explained' in other ways or dismissed as a figment of coincidence. Taken as a whole, however, the case appears, on the face of it, to be a good one. The single notion of continental drift would account, at least qualitatively, for a remarkable number of seemingly unrelated facts, and this, in the final reckoning, is the criterion that we use to judge the *usefulness* (as opposed to the correctness) of an idea. If it can unify and relate a number of diverse observations, it demands at least serious consideration.

Why, then, is one so reluctant to accept the reality of continental drift in the face of this accumulation of evidence? After all, it *could* have been chance that the planets moved about the sun in elliptical orbits; it was only Newton's refusal to accept it as such that led him to the law of gravitation. In the present case, however, the situation is not quite so simple. The precision of the quantitative evidence is much lower; the case so far rests in large measure on the geometrical fitting of irregular shapes and it is difficult to describe such a fit in meaningful numerical terms. Scientific scepticism demands that we be reluctant to accept such a radical conclusion unless it not only fits the facts but is also plausible; unless we can construct a consistent model which will show how it is possible (and indeed probable) for the continents to have moved in this way. Is it reasonable that the continents should drift? Are there forces in the earth that could conceivably produce this? Whatever model is to be constructed must be consistent with all that has been established previously—our imagination is to be constrained and guided by our experience. We shall find that there are cogent objections to the simple models that have been proposed, objections that will have to be overcome before the *idea* of continental drift can become a *theory*.

6.2 CONVECTION IN THE MANTLE: IS IT QUALITATIVELY PLAUSIBLE?

If one is prepared to accept this accumulation of evidence as an indication, if not a proof, of the reality of continental drift, then one must seek a model that will account for it; a description that, with an economy of new hypothesis, is consistent with the constraints that are already established and, if possible, allows the prediction of new relations among properties of the earth that can be tested by observation. It would be less than honest to claim that such a model has been found, one that is satisfactory in all respects, but the search continues. It is an engrossing and exciting one and should it be successful, the rewards in understanding will be great.

Wegener, in his efforts to account for continental drift, invented a westward drift associated with the earth's rotation, but his 'explanation' can no longer be regarded seriously. According to the well-founded laws of mechanics, the continent of America would not of itself drift to the west—something must be present to push it.

A more promising view is that the movements of the continents relative to one another are indications of slow, bodily movements of the underlying mantle, perhaps of the kind associated with convection. Convection is the transfer of heat, not by conduction as in a solid, but by the bodily transport of the material itself and of the heat that it contains. This occurs in heated fluids, and is characterized by rising and falling columns within the fluid. It is seen in the water in a saucepan heated on a stove, in the rising of hot air in an atmospheric thundercloud.

If, in the earth, there are great convection streams in the mantle, rising in some places and sinking in others, as in Figure 54, then near the surface the streams must be horizontal, fanning out

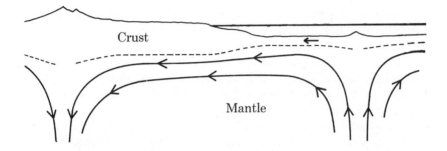

Figure 54. A system of hot rising convection streams (such as the one on the right) may rise from great depths and spread out horizontally, dragging the crust with it. To compensate for the upwelling, there must be other regions (on the left) with a generally sinking stream.

from each rising column and converging to each falling one. Possibly these drag the crust along with them, or even the continents themselves. Before we can ascribe any significance to this suggestion, though, it is necessary to be convinced that movements of this kind in the mantle are qualitatively or descriptively plausible and do not do violence to the observations already established.

The idea poses an immediate dilemma. Convection is a type of motion that can occur only in a fluid. Yet the mantle is capable of transmitting S waves, and these cannot travel through a fluid. Furthermore, deep earthquakes occur frequently at depths between 80 and 300 km, sometimes as deep as 600 or 700 km, and sudden fracture or slipping does not occur in a fluid. These are serious objections; are they crippling? The answer, I believe, is no; by an appeal to a little imagination and experience, it is possible to reconcile these observations with the existence of slow, creeping convection. To do so, however, demands that we consider rather carefully the nature of common materials that we usually call solids.

The simple classification of materials as solids, liquids and gases is convenient, but not particularly precise. Some, like water at ordinary temperatures, are unambiguously liquid. Others, like mayonnaise or the interior of a half-cooked cake are neither clearly solid nor clearly liquid. Sometimes, a material will behave in some respects like a liquid and in others like a solid even though the temperature is the same. One example of this is the material sold as a toy under the name 'Silly Putty.' It can be molded by the fingers like putty; if it is rolled into a ball and dropped, it bounces like an elastic solid; if left on a table, it will gradually sag and spread like a drop of liquid. Another example is pitch. It is hard to the touch; it can be chipped with a hammer. But if a lump of it is left for a few days, it will spread out into a pool—it has not melted, but flowed. Again, mayonnaise in a small jar behaves in some respects like a solid. The jar can be inverted for a short time and the mayonnaise does not flow out. If the jar is then shaken, a lump will break off. Yet it can be spread smoothly, flowing under the greater, steady force applied by a knife.

This general type of behavior, in which the simple classification fails, is in fact very common; it is the rule rather than the exception, especially at the high temperatures that we expect to find in the earth's mantle. Most metals and plastics certainly behave in this way. They can be bent and squeezed into shape; they can be made to *flow*. Even when cold, many materials flow slightly under continual stress, though the rate at which this happens is very much less than it is at high temperatures and so is often imperceptible. The effect is, however, very familiar to the engineer; he calls it 'creep.' In most of these materials, if the stress accumulation becomes too great, it ruptures.

An important property of most of these materials is that under a relatively sudden shock they behave as a solid. The 'Silly Putty' bounces or breaks, the tar chips. On the other hand, under a steadily applied stress (even though it might be quite small) they flow like a liquid. Under their own weight, the pitch and the 'Silly Putty' collapse into a pool.

In summary, then, it appears that many materials have properties that are solid-like and fluid-like in different circumstances. This is particularly true of substances that are not chemically simple. At the high temperatures that we expect in the mantle, *most* materials behave like this. In particular, there is no reason to expect that the chemically complex constituents of the earth's mantle do not. Such a combination of properties, no longer implausible, is, in fact, exactly what is needed to reconcile the seismic observations with the simultaneous existence of slow, creeping convection. The passage of seismic S waves represents a sudden disturbance, and for these the material would behave as a solid. On the other hand, the steady but relentless buoyancy forces produced by heating are applied continually and over times of millions of years; for these the material would behave as a liquid, a very viscous one, certainly, but one capable of flow. If the forces in some location should become too great to be relieved by the flow or should accumulate too rapidly, a rupture may occur and be recorded at the surface as a deep focus earthquake. Why is this unlikely to occur at depths greater than about 600 km? Possibly, one might anticipate that below this, the mantle is rather hotter and less viscous; it can flow more easily to relieve the stress and is less likely to fracture. Possibly the stress accumulations themselves are less or more slowly developed so that rupture is less likely even if the material has the same properties as it does above. Each of these alternatives is consistent with the absence of earthquake foci below this level, but there is no certainty about which, if either, is correct.

Though it may be plausible to attribute deformation properties like these to the mantle material, it should be remembered that we have argued by analogy, that there is no direct evidence that it does, in fact behave in this way. To determine whether or not it does, it would be necessary to obtain a representative sample of the material, to subject it to forces under conditions of high temperature and very high pressure over an extremely long time (thousands or millions of years), and for obvious reasons, the prospects are remote that such experiments will ever be done.

In order to have convection at all, it should be remembered that it is necessary for the mantle to be heated either from below or from within. It was found in the last chapter that a substantial fraction of the surface heat flux apparently comes from the crust or the upper layers of the mantle. This heating from above will not drive convective motions; it can only raise the temperature of the upper layers. In order to increase the temperature of the deep material, to make it lighter and more buoyant than its surroundings, some deep heat source is necessary, and as we have seen, this can comprise at most only a rather small fraction of the total heat generated in the earth. Nevertheless, we shall find that a small fraction may be enough.

One further point about convection should be made. As a general rule, it is a much more efficient way of transferring heat than is conduction alone. Bodily movements carrying fluid from the bottom of the region to the top can be seen to provide a relatively large heat flux even though the average temperature gradient may be quite small. The convection simply stirs the liquid. It was mentioned earlier that the temperature gradient in the earth must of necessity be much smaller in the mantle than it is in the crust. A good deal of this reduction is undoubtedly the result of the concentration of heat sources near the surface, but if there is convective stirring, there is an additional assurance that the temperature gradient in the mantle is necessarily small.

It would appear, then, that a reasonable *prima facie* case, at least at the descriptive level, can be made for the existence of mantle convection. Let us now extend the search a little to see whether there are any other observations for which we can account simply in these terms and whether any other difficulties present themselves either to be overcome, or, perhaps, to force rejection of the whole idea.

6.3 ISOSTASY

It is time now to return to that rather remarkable effect known as isostasy. It will be recalled that this concept developed from detailed gravity measurements at different points on the earth's surface. These indicated that if one adds all the mass per unit area in a column from the surface to some fixed depth below the Moho at its deepest point, then this mass is very nearly the same at all points on the earth, no matter whether the column rises through the ocean, a continental plain or a great mountain range. Where the less dense (and lighter) crust is higher and thicker, the Moho is deeper; the denser mantle material sinks to compensate for the greater mass above. The effect is indeed a striking one, but its interpretation in terms of the model being developed is now almost trivial. If the material of the mantle flows under a steadily applied stress, then the continental land masses will simply subside or rise to the level at which they 'float' on the mantle. Once this balance has been reached, isostasy is an inevitable consequence.

At the very least, then, it is apparent that the existence of isostasy, established by observation, is consistent with mantle properties of the kind that would be associated with convective creep. It is possible to make the statement stronger; if there is to be mantle convection at all with slow creeping flow produced by steadily applied forces, then it is *necessary* that widespread isostasy should be found over the earth's surface.

Here, then, is one point at which our model leads naturally and unambiguously to a prediction entirely consistent with observation. One swallow may not make a summer, but it heartens us to look for more.

The balance implied by isostasy, is, of course, an average one; local departures from it must be expected. The importance of these cannot be overlooked. They are in general of two kinds. There may be a local excess (say) of mass and weight in the crust resulting from topographical irregularities, and these are supported by the strength of the surrounding crust and possibly, to some extent, by the upper mantle. When a ship floats, it is in isostatic balance as a whole—its weight is just balanced by the weight of the water that it displaces. But all of the cargo may be amidships; at this point the mass per unit area of a vertical column may be far in excess of that of the equivalent column of water displaced. *Locally* there is isostatic imbalance, but the strength of the ship supports the extra weight amidships by use of the excess buoyancy fore and aft. The local excursions from isostasy of this kind in regions of the earth that are seismically inactive will clearly give indications about the strength of the crust, of the load that it can support without fracture or flow. If these are too great, of course, rupture will occur. In most seismically active regions there are also relatively large departures or anomalies from isostasy; the associated stresses are evidently too great to be supported by the crust and upper mantle or have accumulated too rapidly to be relieved by flow. Figure 55 shows the anomalies in the earthquake zone of Indonesia, and in many respects, these are typical.

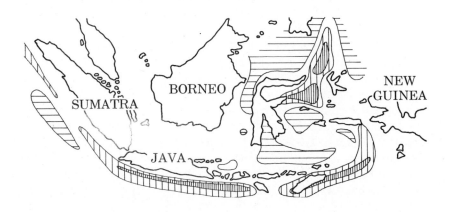

Figure 55. Isostatic anomalies in Indonesia. The horizontal shading indicates regions where the gravitational acceleration g is more than 50 parts per million greater than the average. In the region with open vertical shading, g is between 50 and 100 parts per million *less* than the average, and in those with denser vertical shading, the deficiency is even greater. These anomalies are a small fraction of the average value of g, but they are considerably larger than those found in seismically inactive regions.

Rather different effects are observed when the isostatic anomalies have been produced by a *change* in the surface loading that is relatively rapid when viewed in a geological time scale. At the end of the last ice age, when the polar ice caps receded, the loading (the weight of the ice) on regions such as Scandinavia decreased, and there was an unbalanced net upwards force. The effect of this can still be seen today. Over the Scandinavian peninsula there is a persistent negative isostatic anomaly (a mass deficiency) and at the same time the sea level records of long duration show that the average height of the land is gradually rising relative to the surface of the sea. Relieved of its ice load, the crust is recovering its equilibrium by moving upwards. If a load is lifted from a model boat floating in water, it bobs up very rapidly. If, however, the boat is floating in honey, the recovery is much slower; the more viscous the honey, the longer it takes to regain equilibrium. In Scandinavia, the recovery has taken many thousands of years and is still incomplete, so that the viscosity of the underlying mantle must be very large indeed. In fact, detailed measurements of the rate of rise enable us to calculate a rough value for the apparent viscosity of the material on which the crust is floating. The details of the calculation are not of great interest, but the answer is; the viscosity comes out to be about 10^{22} in c.g.s. units. For comparison, the viscosity of water is about 0.01 c.g.s. units, that of thick honey is about 100 c.g.s. units.

It is, of course, very exciting to be able to calculate the viscosity of the mantle in this way, but the answer should be interpreted with great caution. We already know that just below the crust, many properties of the mantle change quite rapidly with depth, and there is no reason to suppose that the viscosity, in particular, will not. For what depth is this answer of 10^{22} c.g.s. units relevant? Presumably, it is some sort of average over the depth at which the compensating flow takes place, but is it nearer to 100 km or 500 km? The answer is not clear and much debate has been provoked by the ambiguity.

6.4 MOUNTAIN BUILDING

If there are creeping convection currents deep in the mantle and if these can move entire continents, then presumably they are capable of other manifestations that we can observe. It has appeared that the floor of the Atlantic Ocean is possibly being torn apart along the Mid-Atlantic Ridge and carried to the east and the west with America carried along like a patch of foam on a turbulent pool. Presumably, this continual separation is the result of a convective stream, creeping upwards beneath the Mid-Atlantic Ridge and branching to east and west as illustrated in Figure 56. On either side of the ridge the creeping stream in

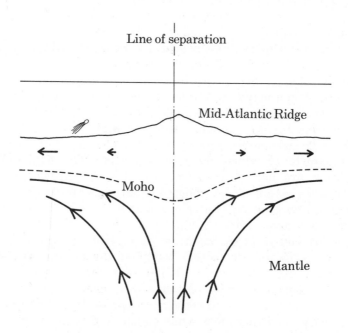

Figure 56. A rising convection column below the Mid-Atlantic Ridge divergence.

the mantle moves horizontally outwards, dragging the crust with it. Along the ridge, the line of separation, one would expect to find a region of high and rapidly accumulating stresses. One would *expect* this to be a seismically active region, and it is. One would *expect* to find an upwards bulge (the Mid-Atlantic Ridge) in the sea floor to counter-balance the 'force' of the stream rising from below.

These expectations are all qualitative. The model of an upwardly creeping convection stream below the crust is descriptively consistent with the continuing separation of the crust, with the existence of a ridge along the line of separation and with the seismic activity there. To see whether the model has any more substantial merit, we should be able to do more—to find *numerical* relations among the quantities involved such as the viscosity of the mantle, the speed and temperature of the stream and the height of the Mid-Atlantic Ridge and, indeed, of other mountains which may be formed as a result of mantle convection. If the results are numerically consistent with observation, then as always, our belief in the idea will increase. If they are not, it will remain a probably erroneous speculation.

We imagine the Mid-Atlantic Ridge as the counter-balance of a rising, very viscous convection stream that is hotter and so more buoyant than its surroundings. The buoyancy force drives the stream upwards and the weight of the Mid-Atlantic Ridge (Figure 57) provides the force necessary to restrain it, to compel the stream to divide and move horizontally to the east and west. This balance of forces gives us a relation between the temperature excess of the vertically rising convection stream in the mantle (which relates to its buoyancy) and the height of the Mid-Atlantic Ridge (which determines the weight of the counter-balance). The detailed derivation is given in Appendix 2.3. From the figures given there, it appears that if the convection column is 300 km deep, then to support a Mid-Atlantic Ridge whose average height is 1000 m as measured, the rising column must be about 100° C hotter than the average temperature of its surroundings. It is rather difficult to judge whether this temperature contrast is reasonable or not. Figure 50 suggests that the difference in the average temperatures between 100 and 600 km is a few hundred degrees, so that it may not strain our credulity too much to find that a stream rising from great depths has a temperature 100° C above the average at the same level. Nevertheless, this first numerical test must be counted as indecisive; we must seek others.

What effects other than the existence of the Mid-Atlantic Ridge might be ascribed to the creeping convection of the mantle? What happens to the horizontal stream as it moves to the west and carries with it all of America? It is not until we

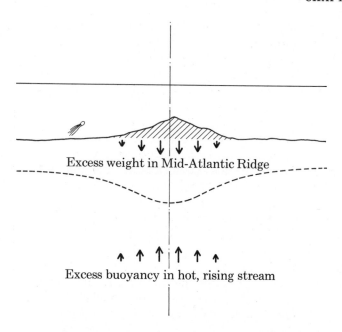

Figure 57. The balance of vertical forces involved in a
convection column below the Mid-Atlantic Ridge—the
excess buoyancy in the stream balancing the excess
weight of the ridge.

reach the Rocky Mountains and the Andes that we encounter any
clue. Where the stream is to plunge downwards (as somewhere
it must), we would expect to find another region of differential
movement of the crust, a concentration of viscous stresses in
the mantle and a piling up of the convected crust. The Pacific
coast is lined by high mountains, it is a region of great seismic
activity: could this be the line of subsidence where the material
of the mantle sinks to be reheated at great depths and to appear, aeons later, beneath the Mid-Atlantic Ridge?

Let us suppose that it is. If the mantle current subsides below
the Rockies, then there is no reason to believe all of the sinking
material comes from the stream flowing westward below the
continent of America. There is some geological evidence (of the
same general nature as that we have described in the Atlantic)

that suggests an *eastward* moving stream beneath the Pacific coast. The two streams converge and sink together (Figure 58); the picture is precisely the reverse of the diverging stream that

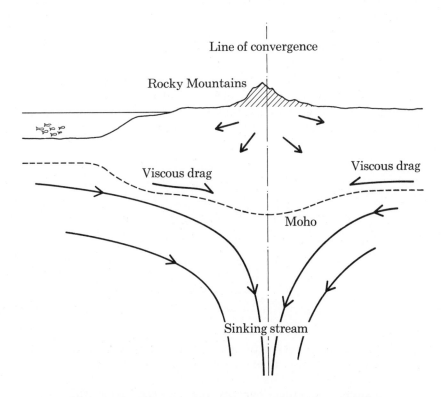

Figure 58. The convergence zone below the Rocky Mountains. The weight of the mountains increases the crustal pressure just below. This acts outwards in all directions and is balanced by the drag of the mantle stream at the base of the crust.

we have imagined below the Mid-Atlantic Ridge. The viscosity of this eastward moving stream drags the continental shelf and the foothills of California with it and drives them against the rest of the continental crust. There is considerable evidence of faulting in this region, indicating that the local stresses have been relieved by fracture. The San Andreas Fault, 600 miles long, is still active. Could the Rockies and the Sierras be the 'pile-up' from such a collision? Naive though this idea is, it again allows a calculation that can be used to evaluate the overall model.

The subterranean pressure produced by the weight of these mountains acts not only downwards to depress the Moho, but outwards horizontally; if they are to be formed by the collision, this outwards pressure must be counter-balanced by the viscous drag produced at the bottom of the continental shelf and the lowlands by the eastwards moving mantle stream before it plunges down. Again (Figure 59), we can make a rough balance

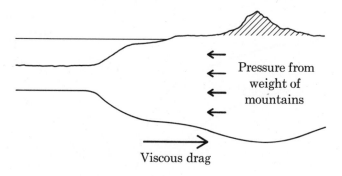

Pressure from
weight of
mountains

Viscous drag

Figure 59. A schematic illustration of the balance of horizontal forces in the crust on the western side of the Rocky Mountains. The viscous drag produced by mantle convection balances the pressure from the weight of the mountains.

of forces to give a connection between the height of the mountains and such things as the width of the coastal region, the viscosity and speed of the creeping mantle. This is given in detail in Appendix 2.4. We can substitute in the relation found there, the numbers for these quantities that have been either inferred from the Scandinavian uplift (which gives the viscosity) and the drift of the Atlantic islands (giving the speed of convection), or else measured directly. In this way, we find that the average height of these mountains should be about 2 km, or 6000 ft. This is quite close to what the height actually is; our model has allowed a *prediction* that is numerically consistent with observation. Hitherto, the most that we could say has been that the convection idea seemed descriptively adequate; now it has managed rather more. It has survived its first quantitative or numerical test.

There are indications of a similar kind of convection eddy beneath the Indian Ocean. This also contains a mid-oceanic ridge, though it is less clearly delineated and more diffuse than that in the Atlantic. It, too, may be a region of divergence, with a drift north and east toward Asia. There, perhaps, it is joined by the eastward current from the Atlantic. The combined stream forces the Indian subcontinent against the mass of Asia and at the point of impact over the line of subsidence rise the great Himalayas. Once more, this region has the characteristics that we expect; the line of high mountains, the isostatic anomalies, the seismic activity.

If the Himalayas are raised by the same process that we have imagined for the Rockies, the same theory of Appendix 2.4 can be used; all that we must do is to substitute the appropriate numbers for this part of the world in order to find the average height of these mountains as well. Because the underlying viscous mantle stream has all of India to drag upon, and not merely the narrow coastal strip of California, the Himalayas piled up by the impact will clearly be higher than the Rockies. Insertion of the actual numerical values leads to the *prediction* that the Himalayas should be, on average, about 6000 m high! This may be a little larger than the actual average height of these mountains, but it is not absurdly large. Mount Everest, the highest peak in the world, is less than 10,000 m above sea level; the average height of the range is possibly 4000 m—smaller than our prediction but well within the uncertainty in the numerical calculations.

Could it be that *all* the major mountain systems of the world were formed as a consequence of mantle convection? If so, and the idea now seems not incredible, then it is apparent that the convection currents must have moved in pattern relative to the continents during past epochs of the earth's history. The Appalachian Range in eastern North America and the Great Dividing Range along the east coast of Australia are old and worn, eroded stumps of their past eminences. Seismically, they are inactive. If each of these was once formed by a convergence line, then clearly it has moved elsewhere long since. The *pattern* of convection itself may not be constant but either wandering or intermittent.

This may well be the means for raising mountains, but it is not the only possibility that has been advanced. If the earth was once much hotter than it is now, then during its cooling, it must have shrunk somewhat. If a solid crust had already formed, then this may have buckled like the skin of a shrunken apple to produce the mountainous zones of the earth. This is a very old idea and much can be said for it. It can be made to account for many of the general properties of mountain systems, at least in a descriptive or semi-numerical way. However, in one crucial quantitative test it appears to fail. If one calculates the rate of shrinking over the lifetime of the earth by assuming a relatively large decrease in average temperature since the crust solidified, one finds that it is just not enough to account for all the buckling observed in the earth's mountains. Possibly, contraction may contribute to the process of mountain building but it is unlikely to be its sole support.

6.5 CONVECTION IN THE MANTLE: A QUANTITATIVE CRITERION

All this presupposes that there *are* in fact convective gyres in the mantle below the crust (Figure 60), an idea to which we have not yet found any qualitative or descriptive objection. The mantle is evidently in a condition that favors convective motion —it is on the average hotter below than above; the hotter and more buoyant material below will tend to rise and the cooler material near the crust to fall. However, whether or not convection will actually occur in a situation like this depends on the viscosity of the mantle; if it is too great in relation to the temperature gradient and the depth of the layer involved, it may not be possible. If the mantle is too viscous, the retarding vis-

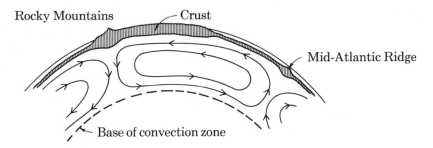

Figure 60. Possible 'gyres' of the creeping mantle convection below North America and the western Atlantic Ocean.

cous forces may win over the buoyancy forces, and any motion may just die away to nothing. The problem of deciding whether convection is or is not possible, is a classical one that has been the subject of intense study since the last century, when it was posed and solved in certain special cases by Lord Rayleigh. It has been found that the occurrence or non-occurrence of convection in a 'fluid' layer like the mantle depends on the size of a rather complicated ratio involving the depth of the layer, the temperature gradient set up by the heating and the physical properties (notably the viscosity) of the 'fluid.' This ratio is usually called the Rayleigh number.

The actual value of the Rayleigh number required to initiate convection is found to depend to some extent on the nature of the boundary surfaces of the layer (whether they are free, like the water surface in a pan, or rigid if the layer is contained between two fixed plates) and on the presence or absence of rotation. In most cases, however, the critical value is about 1000: if convection is to occur in the earth's mantle, the Rayleigh number must be not less than this.

This gives us a firm quantitative criterion for the occurrence of convection in the mantle. If we calculate the Rayleigh number and find it to be larger than about 1000, then convection is not only possible but likely. If it is too small, then convection is not possible and that is the end of the whole matter. Clearly, it is of crucial importance to decide.

The precise form of the ratio is given by

$$R = \frac{\rho E g \beta d^4}{\mu k}, \tag{6.4}$$

where ρ is the average material density, E is the thermal coefficient of expansion of the material, g is the gravitational acceleration, β is the temperature gradient in the region, d is the depth of the layer involved in the convection, μ is the viscosity of the material involved and k is the thermal diffusivity. This is an alternative representation of the conduction coefficient K in Fourier's law, equation (5.2)

$$k = K/\rho C,$$

where C is the specific heat.

In laboratory experiments involving convection, d is usually one or a few centimeters, and for convenient fluids μ is 1 c.g.s. unit or less. In the earth's mantle, d is many kilometers, and it enters R as the fourth power. μ is also very large, but since the *ratio* is involved, a decision cannot be made without substitution of actual numerical values. Most of these we know at least roughly. The least certain are the depths d of the layer and the viscosity μ of the mantle (which we believe to lie between 10^{21} and 10^{23} c.g.s. units). Substitution of reasonable values for the others into equation (6.4) gives as our criterion for convection

$$R = 2 \times 10^{-6} d^4/\mu \text{ must be greater than } 1000. \tag{6.5}$$

No convection occurs when

$$R = 2 \times 10^{-6} d^4/\mu \text{ is less than } 1000. \tag{6.6}$$

The dividing line is shown in Figure 61. Points lying on this line define conditions in which convection is just marginally possible. If given values of d and μ define a point above the line, then for this layer depth and viscosity, convection is possible. If it is below the line, convection cannot occur. Let us consider the range of possibilities.

Suppose first that convection occurs throughout the whole mantle, so that d corresponds to the depth of the mantle-core interface, some 2900 km. Clearly, from the figure, points along

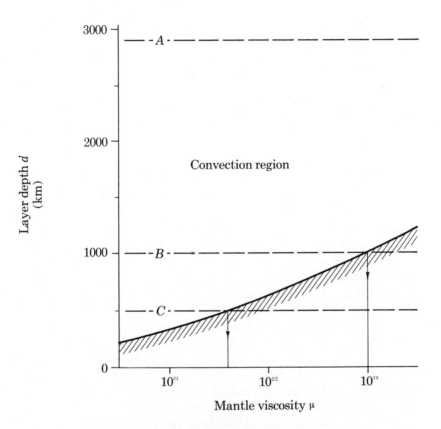

Figure 61. The Rayleigh criterion for convection. Possible depths of the convection zone are plotted vertically, the viscosity of the mantle horizontally. A depth of 2900 km is indicated by the horizontal line A; for all possible values of the viscosity this lies in the 'convection' region of the graph, so that such motions are clearly possible. If the depth is 1000 km (line B) the line is in the convection zone only when the viscosity is less than 10^{23} c.g.s. units. If it is more than this, the line lies in the 'no convection' region and such a motion is not possible. For a layer depth of only 500 km (C), convection will occur only if the viscosity is considerably *less* than 10^{22} c.g.s. units.

this horizontal line are in the convection region, even if the viscosity is at the upper limits of the range suggested. The criterion is satisfied easily.

However, there are indications that convection does not extend to such a great depth. One is the possible existence of a weak discontinuity of some kind at a depth of about 1000 km suggested by the seismic measurements and mentioned at the end of Chapter 4. If this were real, it would be inconsistent with the occurrence of convective streams across this depth; they would stir up the material and cause any discontinuity in constitution to disappear. The second indication comes from the width of the Mid-Atlantic Ridge and other divergence regions. They are only some hundreds of kilometers wide; in nearly all convective motions studied either theoretically or in the laboratory, the widths of these regions are not very much smaller than the depth of the layer itself. Both of these indications suggest (rather indirectly, it is true) that the convective layer may not be as thick as the mantle but considerably less. It may be only 1000 km deep, or even less than that.

If we were to suppose that d is only 1000 km rather than 2900 km, then Figure 61 shows that when the viscosity is as high as 10^{23} c.g.s. units, conditions are now only marginal. We are close to the line; the 'fluid' is almost viscous enough to prevent convection. On the other hand, if the viscosity is less, say our 'best estimate' of 10^{22} c.g.s. units, we are still safe. But finally, suppose that convection takes place in a layer only 500 km thick. This horizontal line in Figure 61 is the lowest of all; if convection is to occur, μ must be *less* than 10^{22} c.g.s. units; this is possible in view of our uncertainty about the actual value of the viscosity μ, but there is little margin of safety.

In summary, then, this criterion shows that convection throughout the whole mantle is clearly possible. If, however, for other reasons we are forced to decide that the convective layer is more shallow, say 500 km, then the criterion can be satisfied only marginally. It lies within our range of possible error; if the viscosity is toward the lower limit of the values that we have calculated, then convection will occur. If it is toward the upper limit, the 'fluid' is too viscous to permit convective motions at all and the whole edifice will collapse.

6.6 DIFFICULTIES

The description of continental drift and its ramifications has become one of great sweep and grandeur. It promises to account for a wide variety of apparently unrelated observations—the fitting of the continental shapes, their apparent movements relative to one another, the division of the crust into oceanic and continental types, the existence of isostasy, the uplifting of Scandinavia and the building of mountains. Not only has it suggested a descriptive interpretation of all these observations; it has already allowed several numerical consistency checks. The Rayleigh criterion does not prohibit mantle convection, at least if the viscosity is small enough but still within the range of possible values. Is it not time to take the vision to our hearts and embrace it with abandon? Our desire may be to do so but there are still difficulties; prudence demands that they be resolved before the consummation is achieved.

One arises from an independent method of estimating the viscosity of the mantle. Over geological time, the rate of spin of the earth about its axis is gradually decreasing—the length of the day is gradually increasing. Careful astronomical observations have enabled this change to be measured quite precisely. Now, as we saw in Chapter 3, the shape of the earth is very close to that which would be assumed by a fluid earth under the competing influences of gravitation and spin. But if the spin is decreasing slowly, the degree of equatorial bulge is also decreasing, though very slowly indeed—the shape of the earth is changing. This change is resisted by viscosity; the viscous forces result in the shape lagging a little behind the one that would be appropriate to the spin, say, now; the earth bulges *very slightly more* than it would if the balance were unchanging. It would appear, then, that a precise measurement of the degree of equatorial bulge (in particular the difference between this and the calculated equilibrium value) would provide a measure of the viscosity resisting the deformation. The measurements require extraordinary accuracy and are near the limit of what can be achieved. Some have been done, however, and have been analyzed by the distinguished American geophysicist G. J. F.

MacDonald and interpreted by him in terms of a homogeneous model of *uniform* viscosity. To account for the difference apparently measured, MacDonald has shown that, in this model, it is necessary that the earth's viscosity be approximately 10^{26} c.g.s. units! This is 1000 times our previous high value; if accurate and relevant, it is so large that the Rayleigh criterion could not be satisfied and convection would *not* be possible.

There are two ways in which this difficulty might be overcome. There may be errors in measurement in the attempt to determine very small differences between the actual equatorial bulge and that which would exist in equilibrium. If the measurements were in error, this would make the calculation a red herring. Again, the assumption of a uniform mantle viscosity to the depth of the core is certainly naive; the top part of the mantle could be considerably *less* viscous if the lower were more viscous. If only a thin layer near the top of the mantle were involved in the readjustment in shape, then it would take place more slowly than if the whole earth were deforming. Very recently, another American geophysicist, L. Knopoff has managed to show that the present shape of the earth is not inconsistent with the existence of a low viscosity (10^{21} c.g.s. units) layer in the upper mantle, some 500 km thick overlying a more viscous region. This may be the answer. Remember that the earlier viscosity measurements *were* concerned with deformation and flow in the upper mantle, not the mantle as a whole. On the other hand, if the convection zone is only 500 km thick, we are close to the critical Rayleigh number for convection, even if the viscosity is as low as 10^{21} c.g.s. units. Because of all the uncertainties, we cannot be assured of convection, but neither can we dismiss it yet on these grounds.

Another really cogent difficulty has also been raised by MacDonald. It is, as we have mentioned in Chapter 5, that the heat flow is substantially the same through the continental crust as it is through the ocean floor. Since most of the heating is apparently in the crust itself, this implies that below the thinner oceanic crust, there must be a greater heat flow than there is beneath the thicker continental one. This is illustrated in Figure 62. To provide this extra heat flow, the mantle, just below the oceans, would have to be considerably more radioactive (or per-

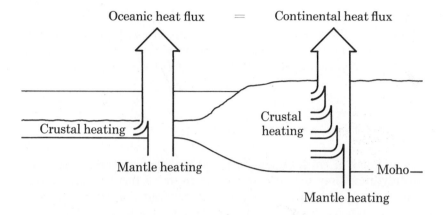

Figure 62. Oceanic and continental heat fluxes. It is observed that the surface heat fluxes are about the same. Some heat comes from radioactive heating in the crust but since the oceanic crust is thinner than the continental crust, it can contribute less. Consequently, more heat must flow from the mantle below the ocean than from the mantle below the continents.

haps intrinsically hotter) than that below the continents. But if there are convection currents in the mantle from beneath the oceans to the continents, how can these differences be maintained? Near the upwelling convection streams, the mantle material may be a bit hotter than in other regions, but hardly enough to provide all the extra heat flow. Convection should stir up the whole mantle; the concentration of radioactive materials should be almost uniform. This is the dilemma. MacDonald considers it to be so serious that the whole idea of mantle convection should be dismissed. Unless and until it can be shown that the radioactive heat sources in the mantle will redistribute themselves in such a way as to give a greater heat flux through the oceanic Moho than they do through the continental Moho, this objection will remain serious. It may, in the end, be crippling.

It may not, however, be necessary to abandon the idea of mantle convection completely; there *are* so many observations with which it is consistent. Possibly the model can be refined or modified in some way so that these difficulties are resolved, though the precise nature of the modification needed is far from clear. The convection model is still in essence, very simple and there is no reason to expect that it contains all of the truth. After all, Nature is often more wonderful than our conception of it.

6.7 FROM AN IDEA TO A THEORY

The ideas of continental drift and mantle convection are most tantalizing. They promise so much: to draw together many different kinds of observations and to account for them, at least in a descriptive way and in some cases in a quantitative way. Yet the existence of mantle convection, which is at the heart of the whole process, is only marginally possible. It is little wonder, then, that the ideas continue to provoke debate that is always vigorous and sometimes acrimonious. Passion has sometimes overcome prudence. Some geophysicists of great repute have embraced the conception, others have denied it, each quoting those observations which appear to support his case and sometimes conveniently overlooking those that do not. Most, however, would admit that the question remains open.

Suppose that we *could* assure ourselves of the existence of mantle convection of a kind that would be consistent with all the firmly based observations that we have, and that we *could* see how the difficulties described in the previous section could be overcome in a natural and consistent way. What else would we demand of the idea before it were to become a Theory? What additional questions would we expect it to answer?

As described at the beginning of this book, an acceptable model must be firmly based—its description must be physically sound and observationally consistent. It must be properly argued; the deductive analysis must be without gaps and *ad hoc* assumptions. The crucial element of its success must be its ability, not only to account for observed 'facts' in a descriptive way but to provide correct numerical relations among them. In these aspects, the development is, at the present time, only partially successful.

A true Theory should provide answers to many other questions. For example, why are the continents characteristically a few thousand miles across and not a few hundred? Why are the land areas of the earth in only four or five great groups and not scattered in small pieces the size of Mauritius or New Guinea? Presumably, it has to do with the size of the convection eddies, but why are they of this size and not some other? If the continental movements are real, why have they moved in this particular way, and not in another? Why are the apparent speeds what they are? If the continents have drifted apart in 300 million years or so, why were they then clumped together on one side of the earth?

To these and many other such questions answers cannot yet be given. If and when they can, an exciting dream will have become a powerful Theory.

7

The Earth's Magnetic Field

7.1 THE EARTH AS A MAGNET

It was possibly the Chinese, a thousand or more years ago, who discovered that if certain pieces of rock containing oxides of iron were suspended freely on a cord, they would align themselves along a north-south direction. One of these minerals is called lodestone, the very name coming from this behavior.* Word of this seems to have returned with the early European travelers who visited China in the 14th century and soon afterwards lodestone compasses were being used by medieval mariners to guide them across the open sea.

In the previous chapter, it was mentioned that many rocks are magnetized to some extent, but lodestone happens to be one in which this effect is particularly strong. It was soon found that if a short rod of soft iron is stroked with lodestone,

---

* Old English *lad:* way, journey or conveyance.

it also becomes magnetic. It will attract other pieces of iron and if hung upon a cord attached to its center, it will swing until it is pointing to the north and south. It is natural and convenient to call the north-seeking end of the magnet the 'north pole' and the other, the 'south pole.'

In 1600, William Gilbert, a physician to Queen Elizabeth, published in his book, *De Magnete,* an account of his experiments and conjectures about magnets. This is a -remarkable work in several respects. It is one of the earliest descriptions of a systematic experimental investigation into any physical phenomenon. In it, Gilbert described making compasses by attaching pointers to small, freely mounted magnets and studying the way that these were influenced by the presence of nearby stronger magnets. He showed that like magnetic poles repel each other and unlike poles attract—the north-seeking pole of his compass was drawn toward the *south* pole of a nearby large magnet and repelled from the north pole. Though Gilbert did not express it in this way, it would appear to us now that the magnetic interaction can be described in terms of a *field* that is conceptually similar to the gravitational field discussed in Chapter 2. It is, of course, a different kind of field, a magnetic field, which in some ways is a little more complicated than a gravitational field. Gravitational interactions are always attractive, whereas both attraction and repulsion are involved in magnetic forces. Moreover, a gravitating mass (the center of the gravitational field) can exist in isolation, whereas magnetic poles, by their very essence (as we shall see), occur in pairs; there cannot be a north pole at one end of the magnet without a south pole at the other. This dual polarity is characteristic of even the simplest magnetic fields; they are known as *dipole* fields, in contrast with the unipolar nature of gravitational fields.

The direction assumed by a compass needle near a large magnet and the net force on it are governed by the balance of four forces—the two attractions between the unlike pairs of poles and the two repulsions between the like pairs. When the compass is very near, say, the north pole of the magnet, as shown in Figure 63(a), the attraction of the south pole of the compass and the repulsion of its north pole are much stronger than interactions with the more distant south pole of the magnet, so that

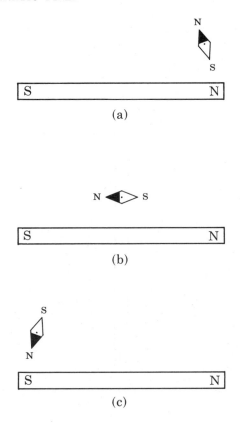

Figure 63. The behavior of a compass needle near a large magnet.

the compass points almost directly toward the pole of the large magnet. When the compass is equidistant from both poles of the magnet (Figure 63(b)), the interaction forces balance and the compass lies parallel to the magnet with its polarity in the opposite sense. As it approaches the south pole of the magnet (Figure 63(c)), the compass experiences more and more strongly the influence of this pole and less and less that of the north pole, so that it gradually swings until its north pole points directly toward the south pole of the magnet. Observations of this kind can be used to plot the directions assumed by a compass at all points in the neighborhood of a magnet, and the lines formed by joining up the directions at different points are shown in Figure 64. These are called lines of force; at any point,

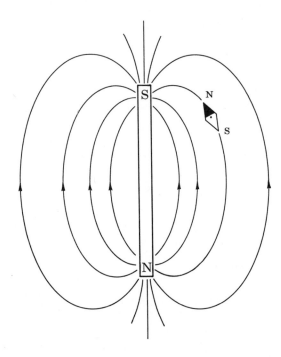

Figure 64. The lines of force of the magnet are formed by joining up the directions assumed by a small compass at various points. They spread out from the north pole of the magnet and converge to the south pole. Arrows can be drawn on the lines of force to show the direction in which the north pole of the compass needle points.

the direction of the line of force indicates the direction assumed by a freely suspended compass.

It would seem, on reflection, that this pattern of lines should hold the clue to the law of force between magnetic poles, the way that the interaction force varies with distance between them. As the compass needle moves toward the north pole of the magnet, the way that it swings toward the pole is a reflection of the increasing interaction forces with that one and the decreasing influence of the other; one might with reason guess that, given sufficient patience and ingenuity, one should be able to infer the force law from this pattern alone. Such is, in fact true, though the geometry involved is rather complicated and may not be to everyone's taste; suffice it to say that the force of interaction between *each pair of poles* is found to vary (as does the gravitational force) as the inverse of the square of the distance between them:

$$F \propto 1/r^2,$$

where $\propto$ means 'is proportional to.' The force depends also, of course, on the strengths of the magnet and the compass; that is, on the magnetic strengths of the poles. The idea of the strength of a magnetic pole can be set up by use of the same type of comparison as was used for the idea of mass. It will be recalled that we compared masses by means of the impact experiments; the choice of one particular mass as a standard or unit of mass enabled us to express the masses of other bodies in terms of this standard. Similarly, by choosing one particular magnet as our standard, the strength of others can be compared with it by a comparison of the forces exerted on a compass needle at some given position.

The basic force law, then, is of the same form as that involved in gravitational attraction, but as a result of the dipole nature of the magnetic field, the total force experienced by each pole of the compass is the sum of the force of attraction between the unlike poles and that of repulsion between the like poles. If the compass is sufficiently far from the magnet, the two can very nearly balance, as in Figure 65, although the individual forces may not be insignificant. The *net* force decreases more rapidly than $1/r^2$. In Appendix 2.5, it is shown that if the distance between the poles of the magnet is d, then far away, the net force on each pole of the compass is of the form

$$F \propto d/r^3, \tag{7.1}$$

decreasing now as the inverse *cube* of the distance r.

This illustrates a principle that will be important later in this

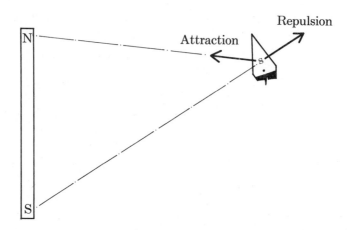

Figure 65. The forces of attraction and repulsion between one pole of the compass needle and a distant
large magnet. If the separation between the two is
fairly large, the distances between the compass pole
and the two poles of the magnet are not very different,
so that the magnitudes of the attractive and repulsive
forces are also about the same. Since their directions
are almost opposite, they tend to balance each other;
the *net* force is smaller than either of the individual
forces.

chapter. The more geometrically complicated a field, the more
rapidly it decays with distance. The forces associated with a
simple unipolar field like gravitation decrease most slowly of
all, as $1/r^2$. Those in a dipole field decrease at great distances as
$1/r^3$. Even more complex fields can be imagined, such as would
be generated by the two equal magnetic dipoles in Figure 66,
parallel but with their orientations reversed. This is a quadrupole field (since four poles are involved); it falls off with distance even more rapidly.

With these things in mind, let us return to Gilbert and his
description of the earth's magnetism. He found that the direction of the field at the surface of the earth is almost indistinguishable from that which would be produced by a huge magnet inside
the earth, whose axis coincides roughly (but not exactly) with

the axis of the earth's rotation. The north-south tendency of a horizontal compass needle is clearly consistent with this, provided the magnetic pole inside the northern hemisphere is actually a 'south-seeking' pole with, of course, the reverse in the southern hemisphere. Even more persuasive were observations on a compass needle mounted to swing in a vertical plane about an east-west axis. This was observed to dip, as in Figure 67, with the north-seeking pole pointing downwards in the northern hemisphere as one would expect from the turning of the lines of force toward the pole of such a subterranean magnet. From these observations, it became apparent to Gilbert that the earth behaved magnetically in a way that is exactly analogous to his

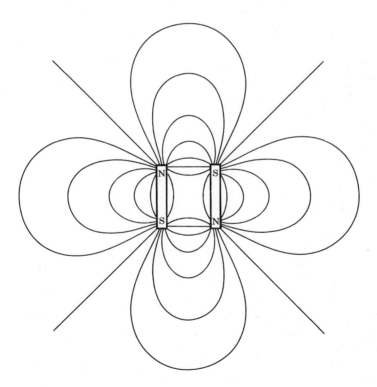

Figure 66. A quadrupole field formed from two equal magnetic dipoles.

North magnetic pole

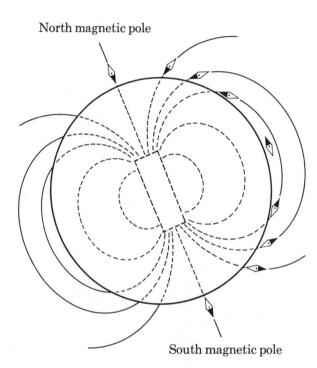

South magnetic pole

Figure 67. The directions of the earth's magnetic field
at the surface. A dip needle (inset) is a compass free
to rotate about a horizontal axis. When the plane of
the instrument is placed in a north-south direction,
the needle dips, showing the inclination of the magnetic field to the horizontal. In the northern hemisphere, the north end of the dip needle points downwards, indicating a convergence of the lines of force
like that which would be produced by a huge subterranean magnet.

laboratory magnet, but on a very much larger scale. In recent years, satellite observations beyond the surface of the earth have confirmed this; to a close approximation, the earth is surrounded by a dipole magnetic field, generated somewhere within it. Far from the earth, to be sure, the field is distorted by the solar wind, the stream of charged particles emanating from the sun, but this is no more than an externally imposed modification quite apart from the generation of the field itself.

The place on the surface of the earth where the north pole of a compass needle points directly downwards is called the north magnetic pole. Its present position is 71° N, 96° W in Prince of Wales Island, Canada. The south magnetic pole is in Antarctica, at 72° S 156° W. It is apparent that these do not coincide with the poles about which the earth rotates and that the earth's magnetic field is tilted a little. The compass, then, does not point exactly north-south, the difference between magnetic north, toward which the compass points, and true north being called the *magnetic declination* (Figure 68). Shortly after Gilbert's time, it was discovered that the magnetic declination varies a little from year to year; in 1580 in London it was 11° E of North while in 1912 it was 16° to the West. This implies that the magnetic poles of the earth wander slowly relative to the true poles, that the earth's magnetic axis shifts. Not only this; the polarity of the earth's field has reversed, possibly several times during the geological history of the earth. This evidence comes from the weak but detectable magnetization of certain lavas and sedimentary rocks, described in the last chapter, the direction of which corresponds to the direction of the earth's field at the time of their formation. Even when allowance is made for continental movement, it would appear that the polarity of successive layers is sometimes reversed in a consistent way at widely separated points. It is difficult to account for this other than by the supposition that the whole field itself has reversed. More recently, it has been found that the field, though very nearly of a dipole nature, is not exactly so; there are in addition small irregularities, both in space over the surface of the earth and in time (varying from one day to the next) at any one point.

These are the primary facts for which we must account. Why does the earth have a slowly wandering, predominantly dipole

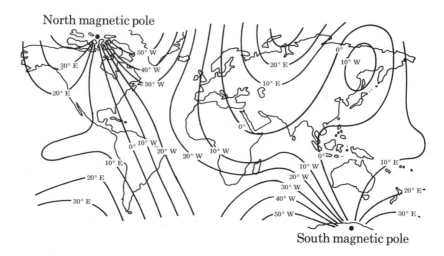

North magnetic pole

South magnetic pole

Figure 68. A simplified chart of the magnetic declinations in 1955. The lines join different places on the earth's surface with a constant declination—that is, a constant angle between true north (the direction of the North Pole) and magnetic north (the direction toward which the compass points). For example, in Florida, the magnetic declination is near zero—the compass points very nearly toward true north. In England, however, it points about 10° to the west of north; in Brisbane, Australia, about 10° to the east of north.

magnetic field, which may occasionally reverse itself? Why is it magnetic at all?

7.2 A 'PERMANENT' MAGNET?

The simplest conjecture might be to suppose that the earth literally *is* a huge permanent magnet similar, apart from its shape, to the laboratory magnets that Gilbert studied. Such an idea is, however, almost certainly wrong. It would be difficult to reconcile it with the observed wandering and possible reversal of the magnetic poles, but there is another property that is even more crippling. This emerges from a consideration of the nature of magnetic materials, from the details of atomic structure that distinguish an unmagnetized bar of iron from the same bar as a magnet.

When a piece of iron is stroked with a magnet until it itself becomes magnetic, there is no discernible change in its gross properties such as density or appearance. Long ago, it was supposed that the distinction was to be found at the atomic or molecular level; that the magnetization or lack of it was a reflection of the order in the atomic arrangement in the material. It was supposed that the atoms themselves behaved as tiny dipole magnets, though why this should be so was not at all clear until this century. The reasons will become apparent in the next section; let us be content for the moment to make the supposition, to explore its consequences rather than its rationale. If each atom is a magnetic dipole with its own magnetic axis, one might imagine that an unmagnetized bar of iron is one in which the individual magnetic axes have no particular directional bias, being oriented quite randomly. The thermal agitation of the atoms would only increase this disorder. The individual atomic dipole fields would then interfere and cancel one another out; there would be no net field associated with the piece of iron as a whole. If, however, the iron is stroked with another magnet, the atomic dipoles, like compass needles, will tend to become aligned with their axes more or less in one direction. When this happens, the individual magnetic fields reinforce rather than cancel; the whole bar becomes magnetized. It can be seen from Figure 69 that once the elementary dipoles are arranged in this way, they tend to remain so, since each north pole is near a neighboring south pole and the mutual attractions resist any turning of a dipole away from its ordered orientation. Several other properties are also evident from this description. The lines of force indicate the direction of alignment of a compass needle, or indeed, any elementary dipole; inside the bar this lies along the axis. Consequently, the interior lines of force run along the length of the bar (Figure 69) emerging at one end and curving back toward the other. Again, since the dipole elements all have their north poles upwards, then so will the bar as a whole, with a south pole necessarily at the other end. Further, if another piece of iron is brought near a pole of the magnet, the

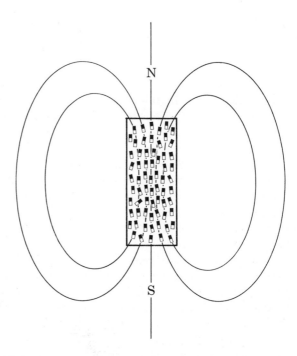

Figure 69. In an unmagnetized bar of iron (top) the
elementary dipoles, whose north poles are shown as
black, are oriented randomly; their magnetic fields cancel out. When the orientations are more orderly, as in
the lower drawing, the elementary fields reinforce
rather than cancel; the bar as a whole becomes magnetic.

randomly oriented elementary dipoles of the iron will experience
magnetic forces which will tend to align *them* also, just as they
do to an isolated compass needle. Magnetism will be *induced* in
the iron by the first magnet and the attraction between the two
is just the attraction between the original magnet and the one
that it induces. When, in the earth, cooling rocks are on the

point of crystallizing, the earth's magnetic field tends to align the weak elementary dipoles of the rock material; when it does crystallize and the temperature drops still further, this alignment is frozen in. This is the *reason* why rock magnetism occurs; it is a weak effect but as we saw in the last chapter, it is one of great importance.

Finally, if the temperature of a magnet is increased, so is the energy of thermal agitation. The atoms assume a more violent motion which may be sufficient to overcome the magnetic restraints tending to retain the alignment of the dipole axes even though the magnet does not melt. When this happens, the orientations begin to wander irregularly; they lose their order and the iron loses its magnetization. The temperature at which this occurs is called the Curie temperature. It can be measured simply by heating a magnet in a furnace until it becomes demagnetized. From such measurements, it is found to be considerably less than the melting point of iron, only some 700° C, a dull red heat.

The Curie temperature is not influenced very much by pressure, and the heart of the earth is certainly much hotter than this. Even if it is made of iron, it is simply too hot to retain any permanent magnetization. The idea of a static magnet inside the earth, then, is quite untenable.

7.3 ELECTROMAGNETISM

It is not only permanent magnets that are capable of generating magnetic fields. In 1819 Oersted, a Belgian physicist, noticed more or less by accident that a straight wire carrying a current of electricity produces a field whose influence is felt by a nearby compass needle. No matter where it is placed, it aligns itself along the tangent to the circle whose center is at the wire (Figure 70) so that the lines of force are simply a series of concentric circles. The orientation in which the compass is observed to point can be remembered by a simple rule. If one imagines an ordinary screw advancing in the direction of the electric current, then the north pole points in the direction of turning. If the direction of the current is reversed, so is that of the compass nee-

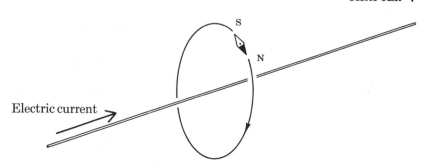

Figure 70. Oersted's Experiment. He found that a freely suspended compass needle always aligns itself along the tangent to the circle centered on the wire, no matter where it is placed. The lines of force are therefore a series of concentric circles about the wire.

dle. Oersted's discovery was the beginning of a brilliant series of achievements by Ampère, Faraday and Maxwell that clarified our understanding of the relations between electricity and magnetism, and provided the basis for much of the technological revolution of the last century, from the generation of electric power to the development of radio.

This is, however, another story, since it is Oersted's discovery that is of primary concern to us now, providing as it does a possible means of generation of the earth's magnetic field without the necessity of a subterranean permanent magnet. If the wire, instead of being straight, is bent into a loop, then at interior points the forces on each pole of the compass are intensified. If, in a cross-section of the loop (Figure 71) the current on the left is flowing inwards, then on the right it is flowing out; both produce the same orientation of a compass needle and the effect is augmented. Outside the loop, the current in the nearby sections influences the compass more strongly than that in distant sections, so that the lines of force turn back, though not now of course in exact circles. Nevertheless, the pattern of lines of force is clearly reminiscent of that shown in Figure 64; apparently a current loop like this can also produce a dipole magnetic field. If the current varies, so does the strength of the field; if it reverses, so does the polarity of the dipole.

This picture provides a link between our earlier description of the iron atoms as elementary dipoles and more modern ideas of atomic structure. In the early years of this century, it became apparent that, in order to account for the spectra of the light emitted by heated (or excited) atoms, each must consist of a small, massive, positively charged nucleus surrounded by clouds

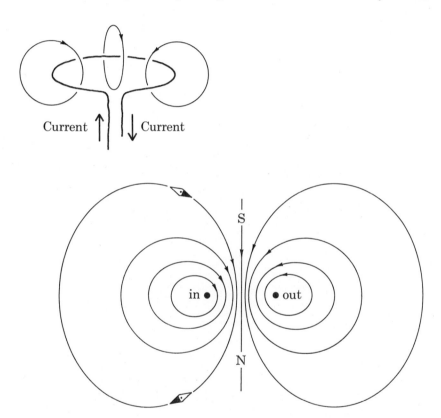

Figure 71. In a wire, carrying current and bent into a loop (top), the magnetic fields at the center reinforce. A cross-section of the loop, shown in the bottom drawing, reveals lines of force which, particularly outside the loop, are strongly reminiscent of those outside a bar magnet. A current loop can generate a magnetic dipole.

of orbiting electrons in concentric shells. Unlike planetary orbits which can be at any distance from the sun, these electron orbits can apparently lie only in certain discrete shells about the nucleus; the realization of this indicated a failure of Newtonian mechanics at these very small subatomic scales and was an important step in the development of a new theory, quantum me-

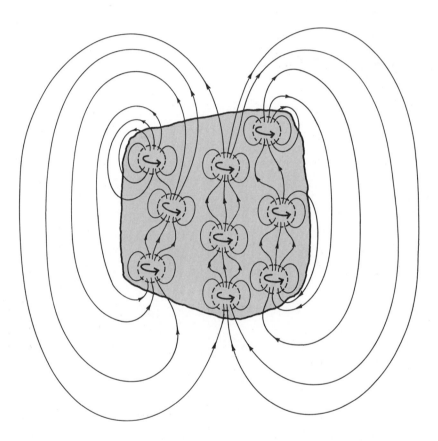

Figure 72. A magnetized piece of iron contains many atomic current loops, all oriented more or less the same way. These are illustrated schematically by the arrows inside the broken circles (the atoms). Inside the material, the lines of force link up; outside it, they curve back to give the whole piece of iron a dipole field.

chanics, to supplement it. Now, if there is a preferred orientation of the electron orbits in a certain group of atoms (Figure 72) with more electrons rotating one way than the other, then they constitute a tiny current loop which, as Oersted showed, generates its own magnetic dipole field. If a substantial fraction of the atoms in a bar are oriented similarly, the bar as a whole will have a dipole field. It would appear from these considerations that 'permanent' magnetism is not after all a separate phenomenon from electromagnetism but is merely a manifestation on a macroscopic or laboratory scale of the ordered orientation of many microscopic or atomic 'electromagnets.'

We have seen, however, that the internal temperature of the earth is too great to permit this kind of ordering on the atomic scale. The magnetic field of the earth could, however, be maintained by a much larger scale ordering; by motions of the core of the earth that result in a circulation of electric current (Figure 73) below the equator and the associated magnetic field with its dipole axis approximately north and south. There may be, in addition, more complicated current circuits which generate more complicated fields, but in accord with our findings in Section 7.1, these decrease in intensity much more rapidly with radius. At the surface of the earth, we would expect that only the far reaching dipole field would remain. The problem that confronts us now is this: How is this equatorial current loop maintained deep inside the earth? There is presumably no battery to drive it; somehow the earth must act as its own dynamo with current produced by internal motions just as it is by the spinning of the various parts in the generator of a car.

7.4 THE EARTH'S DYNAMO

Beyond the fact that it is generated electromagnetically by large scale motions in the earth's core, little is known with certainty about the maintenance of the earth's magnetic field. The details of the motions, the forces that drive them and the way that they ultimately produce the observed field; these are still matters of debate and speculation. The mantle can have little direct role—the motions there that may be responsible for con-

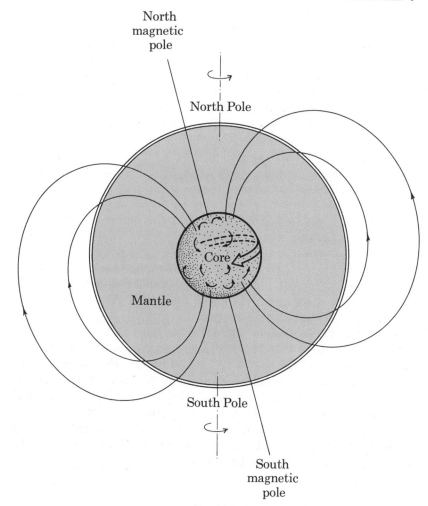

Figure 73. The earth's magnetic field is probably associated with an intense current loop (shown by the
broad arrows) circulating in the core of the earth beneath the equator. The way in which this current is
generated is not known in detail; it is presumably
associated with relatively rapid churning motions of
the iron core (with small arrows).

tinental drift are entirely too slow to be associated with a terrestrial dynamo. The core is another matter—it appears to be liquid, since S waves cannot pass through it—and furthermore to be iron, a good electrical conductor which allows current loops to be established fairly freely. If it is to act as a dynamo, it must be in a relatively rapid churning motion, though what causes this motion is subject to conjecture. One possibility is that there is sufficient heat generation in the core to produce convective eddies. The idea is not free of difficulties—we have already seen that most of the internal heat generation in the earth from radioactive decay is at relatively shallow depths, near the Moho, with possibly some distributed deeper in the mantle giving rise to continental drift. If there *is* heat generation in the core, it must, of necessity, represent only a small fraction of the total heat flux observed at the surface, since most of it has been required to account for other processes. Nevertheless, E. C. Bullard has shown that a convective motion could be driven by as little as a few per cent of the total heat generation in the earth. It may not be unreasonable to suppose that the core might contribute this, but on the other hand, there is no direct indication that it does. Another possibility, advanced recently by W. V. R. Malkus, is that vigorous motions may result from the precession of the earth's axis (Section 3.4). If it is to a first approximation in hydrostatic equilibrium, the core, like the whole earth, will have a slight equatorial bulge. The cavity is filled with liquid, it is spinning rapidly and wobbling slowly, and the combination can, as Malkus has demonstrated, generate surprisingly rapidly churning interior motions. These may well be able to generate the magnetic field, but again, there is no proof yet that they can.

Whatever the actual origin of the motions, it is very likely that the rotation of the earth plays an important part. In Malkus' studies, it is central, but even if the motion is convectively driven, the rotation will certainly have as strong an influence as it does on hurricanes and weather patterns in the atmosphere. It provides an axis, a preferred direction along which the axis of the magnetic dipole will tend to align itself. The argument for this is very simple—the dipole axis must have *some* direction and this is the only obvious one impressed on the motion as a whole. Of course, the dipole axis is observed not to coincide exactly with the rotation axis; the difference must reflect a partial asymmetry in the current distribution below. There is one further scrap of evidence which may be significant. Venus, our nearest neighbor in space, may be structurally similar to the earth, having a liquid core also. But astronomical observations indicate that Venus is spinning very slowly indeed,* so that one of the important ingredients of the dynamo theory is absent. One would expect that Venus should not then have a magnetic field, not, at least, one generated in this way. The first Mariner satellite to fly by Venus searched for a magnetic field and found none. This does not, of course, prove that any of these ideas about the earth's dynamo are correct; there could be some quite different process involved, and the fact that Venus spins very slowly may have nothing to do with the matter one way or the other. Nevertheless, it does offer a scrap of consistency and for this we must be grateful.

7.5 IN RETROSPECT

Gradually, throughout this book there has emerged a way in which the various parts of the puzzle appear to fit together; the models devised apparently represent some degree of physical reality. Some of the models have been tested repeatedly and found reliable; they offer a cornerstone on which we can safely build. If we grant the existence of gravitation, if we ask not *why* there is gravitation but *what are its consequences,* then the theory is of remarkable generality and accuracy. Other models have not yet acquired this degree of credence; they appear to be self-consistent and to provide a few quantitative relations between different kinds of observations, but not many. Our ideas of the internal structure of the earth are of this kind; while apparently sound in their broad features, they lack the simplicity, precision and extent of application characteristic of the laws of mechanics and gravitation. Others are tentative and still unformed; an outline of a model may be discernible but the details are indistinct.

---

* About once in 243 terrestrial days.

In the case of continental drift, there is an accumulation of circumstantial evidence; yet there is still the difficulty of convincing ourselves beyond question that such a thing *must* occur. The existence and nature of the earth's magnetic field is beyond dispute, but the purely mathematical and physical complexities of the problem have, in spite of great effort, defied solution. Different aspects of these models are in different stages of completion; while our efforts continue, they will be refined, modified or discarded.

The clues that we have about the nature of the heart of the earth are few, but enough to make the imagination search where the eye cannot see. Nature reveals herself shyly and in many disguises; we must have the wit to perceive her and the patience to understand.

Appendix 1

METRIC UNITS AND EQUIVALENTS

The basic units of length, mass and time in the metric system are, respectively, the centimeter, gram and second; for this reason it is sometimes known as the c.g.s. system. Units in this system can be called simply 'c.g.s. units,' without regard to their precise nature (whether they are units of force, velocity or something more complicated). The table below gives relations between the various quantities used in this book.

Measures of Length:

100 centimeters (cm) $= 10^2$ cm $= 1$ meter (m)
1000 meters $\qquad = 10^3$ m $\ = 1$ kilometer (km)
100,000 cm $\qquad = 10^5$ cm $= 1$ km

Approximate Equivalents:

2.54 cm $= 1$ inch
1 m $\quad = 39.36$ inches
1 km $\ = \frac{5}{8}$ mile

Measures of Mass:

1000 grams (gm) $= 10^3$ gm $= 1$ kilogram (kg)

Approximate Equivalents:

28 gm $= 1$ ounce
1 kg $= 2.2$ lb.

Measures of Time:

These are the familiar seconds, minutes, hours, etc.

A note on indicial notation: 10^3 means ten multiplied by itself three times, or 1000. Similarly, $10^2 = 100$, etc. To multiply two such indicial numbers, we simply *add* the indices:

$$10^2 \times 10^3 = 10^5,$$

which is,

$$100 \times 1000 = 100,000.$$

The symbol 10^{-3} represents the inverse of 10^3, namely $1/10^3$ or $1/1000$. The same multiplication rule holds. For example,

$$10^4 \times 10^{-3} = 10^1 = 10$$

or, in more familiar notation,

$$10,000 \times \frac{1}{1000} = 10.$$

Finally, 10^0 can be interpreted as just unity. For

$$
\begin{aligned}
10^0 &= 10^{(1-1)} \\
&= 10^1 \times 10^{-1} \\
&= 10 \times \frac{1}{10} \\
&= 1.
\end{aligned}
$$

Appendix 2: Some Detailed Derivations

2.1 THE MOTION OF A SIMPLE PENDULUM (SECTION 2.3)

Suppose that a pendulum bob of mass m is suspended from a fixed point by a light string of length l, and that at some instant the string makes an angle θ with the vertical (Figure A.1). Our object is to set up a balance, according to Newton's laws of motion, between the net force acting on the bob and its instantaneous mass-acceleration. This will provide an equation whose solution specifies the way in which the angle θ changes with time and, in particular, the time taken for the pendulum to complete its swing.

The first step is to find the net force acting on the bob when it is displaced from the vertical. There are two clearly identifiable forces involved—the tension S in the string and the weight of the bob, mg, acting vertically downwards. Since the string is not exactly vertical, these do not quite balance, and the imbalance or *net* force provides the inwards acceleration of the bob. Now,

215

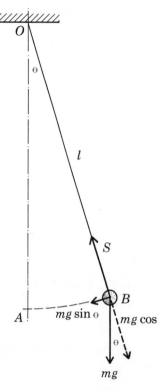

Figure A.1. The forces involved in the swinging of a
pendulum. The tension S
acts along the line of the
string and the weight mg
vertically downwards. This
is equivalent to a part (mg
$\cos \theta$) acting along the line
of the string together with
another component, mg
$\sin \theta$, toward A. It is this
latter part that produces
the inwards acceleration.

the direction of motion is always perpendicular to the string;
what is the force in this direction? The tension S acts along the
string—it has no component in this direction. The weight mg,
however, acts vertically downwards, at an angle θ to the string,
so that the component of this force (Figure A.1) is $mg \sin \theta$,
acting toward the rest position A. It is convenient to regard the
direction to the right as positive, so that the net force is given
by

$$F = -mg \sin \theta, \qquad (A.1)$$

acting to the right.

The next task is to find the acceleration of the bob in terms of
θ, so that we can set up the balance required by Newton's laws.
The distance along a slightly curved arc AB is $l\theta$ where θ is meas-

ured in radians. The velocity of the bob is the rate of change of this length with time; in the notation of differential calculus,

$$\frac{d}{dt}(l\theta) = l\frac{d\theta}{dt},$$

since the length l is constant. The acceleration is the rate of change of this velocity:

$$\frac{d}{dt}\left(l\frac{d\theta}{dt}\right) = l\frac{d^2\theta}{dt^2},$$

measured in the direction of θ increasing (i.e., to the right). The mass-acceleration, then, is

$$ml\frac{d^2\theta}{dt^2}. \tag{A.2}$$

Finally, we must balance the net force by this mass-acceleration. From equations (A.1) and (A.2),

$$-mg\sin\theta = ml\frac{d^2\theta}{dt^2}.$$

We can divide both sides by ml, whence

$$\frac{d^2\theta}{dt^2} + \frac{g}{l}\sin\theta = 0. \tag{A.3}$$

This is called a differential equation, the solution of which specifies the way that the angle θ changes with time as the pendulum swings. Notice that m has dropped out of the equation; the mass of the bob is therefore irrelevant to the motion.

Although equation (A.3) does not seem to be very complicated, it is nevertheless impossible to find a general solution to it in terms of simple mathematical functions. If, however, we restrict the motion to one in which the maximum angle of swing is *small*, then we can approximate to (A.3) and find the solution quite easily. The key step is that when the angle θ is always small (compared with 1 radian, about $57°$), $\sin\theta = \theta$, very nearly, so that under these conditions, (A.3) can be written

$$\frac{d^2\theta}{dt^2} + \frac{g}{l}\theta = 0, \tag{A.4}$$

which is now much easier to solve. There is, of course, a systematic way of solving equations of this kind, but the simplest technique is to guess a form of solution and then test to see whether it indeed satisfies the equation.

We know that as time t goes on, the pendulum swings back and forth; the angle θ is an oscillating function of time. The simplest such function is the sine or cosine; let us try as a solution

$$\theta(t) = A \cos (2\pi t/T),\qquad\qquad (A.5)$$

where A is the maximum angle of swing; $\theta(t)$ varies between $\pm A$ as $\cos (2\pi t/T)$ varies with increasing t between ± 1. Notice that when $t = 0$, $\theta = A$, and when $t = T$, $\theta = A \cos (2\pi T/T) = A \cos 2\pi = A$ again; the cycle is complete. Accordingly, T represents the *period* of the pendulum (Figure A.2).

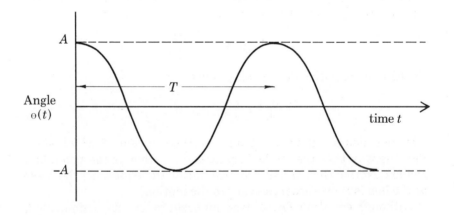

Figure A.2. The angle of swing of a pendulum, plotted vertically, as a function of time. The period T is the time taken for a complete cycle, during which the argument of the cosine function advances by 2π.

Under what conditions does (A.5) satisfy the equation (A.4)? By differentiation of (A.5),

$$\frac{d\theta}{dt} = -A \left(\frac{2\pi}{T}\right) \sin \left(\frac{2\pi t}{T}\right),$$

and differentiation again

$$\frac{d^2\theta}{dt^2} = -A\left(\frac{2\pi}{T}\right)^2 \cos\left(\frac{2\pi t}{T}\right).$$

Substitution from this and (A.5) into (A.4) gives

$$-A\left(\frac{2\pi}{T}\right)^2 \cos\left(\frac{2\pi t}{T}\right) + \frac{g}{l} A \cos\left(\frac{2\pi t}{T}\right) = 0,$$

which must be true for all t. If we divide this last equation by A $\cos(2\pi t/T)$, we have

$$-\left(\frac{2\pi}{T}\right)^2 + \frac{g}{l} = 0,$$

or

$$T = 2\pi(l/g)^{1/2}. \tag{A.6}$$

This specifies the period T in terms of l and g as stated by equation (2.10). Notice that A also has disappeared; the period of the pendulum is independent of both the mass m and of the amplitude of swing A.

2.2 A SIMPLE EARTH MODEL (SECTION 3.5)

The task is to find expressions for the average density and moment of inertia coefficient of the two-layer model (Figure 20) in terms of the radii $\mathcal{R}$ and $\mathcal{R}'$ and the densities ρ_1, ρ_2; to use the values that we already know to calculate the unknowns $\mathcal{R}'$ and ρ_2.

Regarding it as a sphere, the volume of the whole earth is $\frac{4}{3}\pi\mathcal{R}^3$, while the volume of the inner region is $\frac{4}{3}\pi\mathcal{R}'^3$. The volume of the outer part is the difference between the two, namely

$$\frac{4}{3}\pi(\mathcal{R}^3 - \mathcal{R}'^3).$$

Now, the density of the outer region is ρ_1, so that its total mass is

$$\frac{4}{3}\pi\rho_1(\mathcal{R}^3 - \mathcal{R}'^3).$$

The inner region has density ρ_2; its mass is therefore

$$\frac{4}{3}\pi\rho_2\mathcal{R}'^3.$$

Adding these two gives the total mass of the earth,

$$\frac{4}{3}\pi[\rho_1(\mathcal{R}^3 - \mathcal{R}'^3) + \rho_2\mathcal{R}'^3].$$

But if the average density of the earth is $\bar{\rho}$ $(= 5.5)$, then the total mass can be written alternatively as

$$\tfrac{4}{3}\pi\bar{\rho}\Re^3.$$

These last two can be equated, and after cancellation of $\tfrac{4}{3}\pi$, we have

$$\bar{\rho}\Re^3 = \rho_1(\Re^3 - \Re'^3) + \rho_2\Re'^3. \tag{A.7}$$

This is one relation among the unknowns—one constraint that they must satisfy.

The second involves the moment of inertia. For a uniform solid sphere, the moment of inertia is given by equation (3.9) as

$$I = \tfrac{2}{5}m\Re^2.$$

The inner region has mass $\tfrac{4}{3}\pi\rho_2\Re'^3$ and radius $\Re'$; its moment of inertia is

$$\tfrac{2}{5}\cdot\tfrac{4}{3}\pi\rho_2\Re'^5.$$

The outer region does not include the hole in the middle; to find *its* moment of inertia, we can subtract from the value that it would have if it were solid and uniform the part contributed by the central region which is not there:

$$\tfrac{2}{5}\cdot\tfrac{4}{3}\pi\rho_1\Re^5 - \tfrac{2}{5}\cdot\tfrac{4}{3}\pi\rho_1\Re'^5 = \tfrac{2}{5}\cdot\tfrac{4}{3}\pi\rho_1(\Re^5 - \Re'^5).$$

The total moment of inertia is therefore

$$\tfrac{2}{5}\cdot\tfrac{4}{3}\pi[\rho_1(\Re^5 - \Re'^5) + \rho_2\Re'^5],$$

which we know is equal to $0.3337\, m\Re^2$ where $m = \tfrac{4}{3}\pi\bar{\rho}\Re^3$ is the total mass. If these two are equated, then, and we divide by $\tfrac{4}{3}\pi$, there results

$$0.4[\rho_1(\Re^5 - \Re'^5) + \rho_2\Re'^5] = 0.3337\bar{\rho}\Re^5, \tag{A.8}$$

our second relation of constraint.

These two equations can be simplified a little by the substitution

$$r = \Re'/\Re,$$

whence from (A.7),

$$\bar{\rho} = \rho_1(1 - r^3) + \rho_2 r^3,$$
$$= \rho_1 + (\rho_2 - \rho_1)r^3, \tag{A.9}$$

and from (A.8),

$$0.3337\bar{p} = 0.4[\rho_1(1 - r^5) + \rho_2 r^5],$$
$$0.834\bar{p} = \rho_1 + (\rho_2 - \rho_1)r^5. \tag{A.10}$$

Now $\bar{p} = 5.5$ and $\rho_1 = 2.8$, so that from (A.9),

$$5.5 = 2.8 + (\rho_2 - \rho_1)r^3,$$
$$(\rho_2 - \rho_1)r^3 = 2.7. \tag{A.11}$$

Similarly, from (A.10),

$$2.8 + (\rho_2 - \rho_1)r^5 = 0.834 \times 5.5$$
$$= 4.6,$$
$$(\rho_2 - \rho_1)r^5 = 1.8. \tag{A.12}$$

Now, divide (A.12) by (A.11):

$$\frac{(\rho_2 - \rho_1)r^5}{(\rho_2 - \rho_1)r^3} = \frac{1.8}{2.7},$$
$$r^2 = 0.667,$$
$$r = 0.82 = \Re'/\Re.$$

Finally, we substitute this value for r back into either (A.11) or (A.12). From (A.11), say,

$$\rho_2 - \rho_1 = \frac{2.7}{r^3} = \frac{2.7}{(0.82)^3} = 4.9,$$

so that

$$\rho_2 = 4.9 + \rho_1 = 4.9 + 2.8 = 7.7.$$

These are the results given in equation (3.11) and illustrated by Figure 21.

2.3 THE HEIGHT OF AN OCEANIC RIDGE (SECTION 6.4)

What is the height of an oceanic ridge that can be supported by the buoyancy of an underlying hot rising stream in the mantle? Suppose the stream has a temperature θ hotter than the average mantle temperature at that depth; if the coefficient of volumetric expansion is E, then a cube of unit mass in the rising column is larger than one outside it by a fractional amount $E\theta$;

its density is *smaller* by the fraction $E\Theta$. The density in the rising column is therefore $\delta\rho = \rho_m E\Theta$ *less* than that of the surrounding mantle, whose density is ρ_m. If d is the depth of the hot column, the mass deficiency per unit area is $\rho_m E\Theta d$. The buoyancy force upwards per unit area is this mass deficiency times the gravitational acceleration:

$$F = \rho_m E\Theta dg. \tag{A.13}$$

This, we suppose, balances the excess weight of the ridge. If h is its height and ρ and ρ_w the densities of the ridge and the surrounding water, the excess mass per unit area in the ridge is $(\rho - \rho_w)h$ per unit area, and the excess weight is

$$W = (\rho - \rho_w)gh. \tag{A.14}$$

Equating (A.13) and (A.14) gives

$$(\rho - \rho_w)gh = \rho_m E\Theta dg,$$

or

$$h = \frac{\rho_m E\Theta d}{(\rho - \rho_w)}.$$

Now, in round numbers, $\rho = \rho_m = 3$, $\rho_w = 1$, and for most rocks E is approximately 2×10^{-5} per centigrade degree. Thus

$$h = \frac{3 \times 2 \times 10^{-5}}{2}\Theta d$$

$$= 3 \times 10^{-5}\Theta d.$$

If $d = 300$ km and $h = 1$ km, then Θ is approximately $100°$ C; the rising column must be about $100°$ C hotter than its surroundings.

2.4 THE HEIGHT OF CONTINENTAL MOUNTAINS (SECTION 6.4)

Suppose h represents the height of the mountain range formed by the collision of a coastal region with width L against the continental mass. The mass per unit area in the range is ρh, where ρ is the density of the rock, and the weight per unit area, the pressure at the base of the mountain is ρgh. This pressure acts outwards over the depth D of the crust (Figure 59); the total force per unit length of the range is then ρghD.

The mantle stream moving to the right exerts a viscous drag on the bottom of the crust. If the viscosity of the mantle is μ and the stream is of depth l, moving with speed U, then this viscous drag is known from fluid mechanics to be approximately $\mu U/l$ per unit area. The width of the coastal zone is L, so that the total viscous force per unit width is $\mu UL/l$.

These two forces must balance, so that

$$\rho ghD = \mu UL/l,$$

or
$$h = \frac{\mu UL}{\rho gDl}. \tag{A.15}$$

If we take $\mu = 10^{22}$ c.g.s. units, $U = 2 \times 10^{-7}$ cm/sec, $\rho = 3$, $g = 10^3$ c.g.s. units, and $D = 30$ km $= 3 \times 10^6$ cm, then

$$h = \frac{10^{22} \times 2 \times 10^{-7}}{3 \times 10^3 \times 3 \times 10^6} \frac{L}{l},$$

$$= 2 \times 10^5 \frac{L}{l}, \text{ approximately.}$$

In California, L is about 300 km; taking the depth l as 300 km also, then $L/l = 1$ and

$$h = 2 \times 10^5 \text{ cm},$$
$$= 2000 \text{ m.}$$

In India, L is about 1000 km, and for the same depth l of the convection stream,

$$h = 6000 \text{ m,}$$

as given in Section 6.4.

2.5 THE FORCE FIELD
OF A MAGNETIC DIPOLE (SECTION 7.1)

To show that the net force on each pole of a compass needle in the presence of a magnetic dipole is proportional to $1/r^3$, consider the geometrically simple situation shown in Figure A.3. The north pole of the compass is equidistant from the two poles

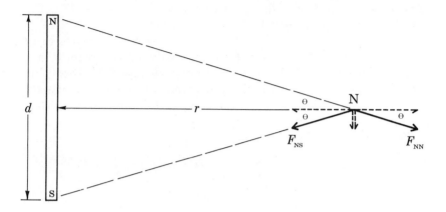

Figure A.3. The forces between one pole of a compass needle and a magnetic dipole. Each of the forces F_{NN} and F_{NS} of repulsion and attraction can be considered to have components toward and away from the dipole center (which balance) and downwards (which add).

of the magnet and the forces of repulsion F_{NN} and attraction F_{NS} are each proportional to $1/r^2$ and are in the directions shown. Their magnitudes are the same so that the components of the two forces toward and away from the center of the magnet balance exactly. The components in the downwards direction, however, add.

The component of F_{NN} downwards is $F_{NN} \sin \theta$, and since from the geometry of the larger triangles on the right,

$$\sin \theta = \frac{\frac{1}{2}d}{[r^2 + (\frac{1}{2}d)^2]^{1/2}},$$

this component is

$$\frac{F_{NN}d}{(4r^2 + d^2)^{1/2}}.$$

The downwards component of F_{NS} is precisely the same, so that the total force on the north pole of the compass is

$$\frac{2F_{NN}d}{(4r^2 + d^2)^{1/2}}.$$

But F_{NN} itself is proportional to the inverse square of the distance between the two north poles, i.e., to

$$4/(4r^2 + d^2),$$

so that the net force of interaction (downwards) is proportional to

$$\frac{d}{(4r^2 + d^2)^{3/2}}.$$

Far from the magnet, when r is much greater than d, $4r^2 + d^2 \simeq 4r^2$ and the net force is proportional to d/r^3, as given by equation (7.1).

A Short Bibliography

Anderson, D. L. The plastic layer of the earth's mantle. *Scientific American*, July 1962, pp. 52–59.

Bullard, E. C. The flow of heat through the floor of the ocean. *The Sea* (ed. M. N. Hill), Vol. 3, pp. 218–32. New York and London: Interscience Publishers, 1963.

Bullard, E. C., and Gellman, H. Homogeneous dynamos and terrestrial magnetism. *Phil. Trans. Roy. Soc.*, *A247* (1954), pp. 213–78.

Bullard, E. C., and Mason, R. G. The magnetic field over the oceans. *The Sea* (ed. M. N. Hill), Vol. 3, pp. 175–217. New York and London: Interscience Publishers, 1963.

Bullen, K. E. *Introduction to the Theory of Seismology*. Cambridge University Press, 1947. (An introduction at an advanced level.)

Ewing, J. I. The mantle rocks. *The Sea* (ed. M. N. Hill), Vol. 3, pp. 103–9. New York and London: Interscience Publishers, 1963.

Gutenberg, B. (ed.). *The Internal Constitution of the Earth.*

New York: Dover, 1951. (A compilation of essays by distinguished geophysicists, written at a moderately advanced level.)

Heirtzler, J. R., le Pichon, X., and Baron, J. G. Magnetic anomalies over the Reykjanes Ridge. *Deep-Sea Research, 13* (1966), pp. 427–44.

Holmes, A. *Principles of Physical Geology.* London and Edinburgh: Nelson, 1945. (In the original edition of this work, now a classic, Holmes advanced the idea of mantle convection and its association with continental movements.)

Jeffreys, H. *The Earth.* Cambridge University Press, 1947. (Also a classic, on the physics of the earth.)

Magnetism of the Earth. U. S. Dept. of Commerce, Coast and Geodetic Survey. Washington, D. C. Publication no. 40-1 (1962).

Menard, H. W. Sea floor spreading, topography and the second layer. *Science, 157* (25 August 1967), pp. 923–4.

Oliver, J., and Dorman, J. Exploration of sub-oceanic structure by the use of seismic surface waves. *The Sea* (ed. M. N. Hill), Vol. 3, pp. 101–33. New York and London: Interscience Publishers, 1963.

Phillips, J. D. Magnetic anomalies over the Mid-Atlantic Ridge near 27° N. *Science, 157* (25 August 1967), pp. 920–3.

Runcorn, S. K. (ed.). *Continental Drift.* New York and London: Academic Press, 1962. (Complements the Royal Society *Symposium,* below.)

Shapiro, I. I. Resonance rotation of Venus. *Science, 157* (28 July 1967), pp. 423–5.

Symposium on Continental Drift. London: The Royal Society. (*Phil. Trans. 1088*), 1965. (A comprehensive survey of various aspects of continental drift, particularly the newer evidence of drift and possible mechanisms.)

Takeuchi, H., Uyeda, S., and Kanamori, H. *Debate about the Earth.* San Francisco: Freeman, Cooper & Co., 1967. (A fine descriptive account of the earth's structure and geological history, centered about the debate concerning continental drift.)

Theory of Continental Drift; A Symposium. Tulsa: American

Association of Petroleum Geologists, 1928. (A strong rejection of the early ideas of continental drift.)

Wegener, A. *The Origin of Continents and Oceans.* Translated by J. Biram. New York: Dover, 1967. (A translation of the fourth edition, 1929, presenting Wegener's mature ideas.)

Wilson, J. T. Continental drift. *Scientific American,* April 1963, pp. 86–100.

Index

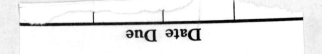
Date Due